DIVISION

Twin 250CD
718451025021
ISBN-10: 1-57583-895-8
ISBN-13: 978-157583-895-3

Credits:

Publisher: Twin Sisters Productions, LLC
Executive Producers: Kim Mitzo Thompson, Karen Mitzo Hilderbrand
Music By: Kim Mitzo Thompson, Karen Mitzo Hilderbrand, Hal Wright
Music Arranged By: Hal Wright
Workbook Authors: Kim Mitzo Thompson, Karen Mitzo Hilderbrand, Ken Carder
Book Design: Steven Dewitt

www.twinsisters.com   1-800-248-TWIN(8946)

Table of Contents

How To Use This Division Music CD & Workbook

Music makes learning fun and easy! We're confident that the songs and activities included in this 96-page Workbook and Music CD set will make learning division a bit easier...and definitely a bit more fun.

The Music CD includes original songs that teach division facts 0 through 9 and several strategies that help many students better understand the concept of division. The lyrics to the songs are included in this book. Encourage your child to listen to the music CD each day for a week or longer. Listen together in the car!

This workbook features explanations, practice worksheets, learning games, and challenges that introduce and reinforce division facts 0 through 12, advanced division without and with regrouping. The learning activities can be used alone or with a partner—or even an entire classroom! Make photocopies of the pages for repeated practice.

Children should have addition, subtraction, multiplication, and division facts at their fingertips before they leave elementary school. For some, memorization comes easy. For others, memorization is much more difficult. In all cases, memorization must follow an understanding of the concept. Look for ways to count, combine, sort, and divide objects. Look, too, for patterns and reasoning or strategies that help your child understand division.

Listen and learn the songs together. Complete the worksheets and play the games together. Above all, enjoy the time together.

Words to Understand!

DIVISION: An operation that separates a unit into parts.

DIVIDEND: The quantity you are dividing.

DIVISOR: The number you are dividing into the **DIVIDEND**.

QUOTIENT: The answer in division; the result of dividing a **DIVIDEND** by a **DIVISOR**.

REMAINDER: The amount left over after dividing.

Division Terminology

Today, we are going to learn the correct terminology used in division. Terminology is the vocabulary of technical terms used in a particular field. So, when we're learning about division, three words that are important to know are quotient, divisor, and dividend.

Quotient, divisor, and dividend–
terminology I recommend.
Let's learn what each word really means;
it will help us talk intelligently.
It's division terminology–
words we need, I guarantee,
when we're talking about math.
When we're learning our facts,
these words will have a great impact!

A **quotient** is the number obtained by dividing one quantity by another. In 24 ÷ 6 = 4, 4 is the quotient. The quotient is the answer to a division problem.

The quotient is the answer
when we're learning to divide.
Take 12 ÷ 3
now 4 is the answer you will find.

(Chorus)

A **divisor** is a quantity that evenly divides another quantity. In 24 ÷ 6 = 4, 6 is the divisor. Remember that a divisor is a quantity that evenly divides, so while 6 is a divisor of 24, 6 is not a divisor of 25.

A divisor is a quantity that
evenly divides another quantity,
on this you can rely.

(Chorus)

A **dividend** is a number or quantity which is to be divided. So in the problem 24 ÷ 6 = 4, 24 is the dividend.

A dividend is a number
which is to be divided.
I'm told that they're the words
mathematicians have decided.

(Chorus)

Rules of Zero

(It's easy to divide with the number zero. Just remember these two simple rules: you can divide into zero, but you can't divide by zero. For example, $0 \div 6 = 0$, but $6 \div 0$ can't be done.)

Divide by zero–NO WAY!
Divide by zero–NO WAY!
Divide by zero–it can't be done.
It's the zero, zero, zero mathematical fun.
For zero divided by any number is 0!

$0 \div 5$ is 0

$0 \div 10$ is 0

$0 \div 100$ is 0

For zero divided by any number is 0!

It's the zero, zero, zero mathematical fun.
You can't divide by zero. It just can't be done.
So remember, zero divided by any number is 0!

What about?

$0 \div 263$? 0!

$0 \div 494$? 0!

$0 \div 927$? 0!

Okay, what about 0 divided by 1,269,438?
0! 0! 0!

(Chorus)

It's the zero, zero, zero mathematical fun.
You can't divide by zero. It just can't be done.
So remember, zero divided by any number is 0!

(Chorus)

Okay, what about 1,238,497,632?
ZERO!

Any Number At All

Any number, I mean any number–
it could be any number at all–
any number divided by one
is that same number.
(Repeat)

(Chorus 1:)
Any number at all,
could be big or small,
could be a one- or two-digit number,
for the only thing to remember
is that ANY number divided by one
is that same number.

$5 \div 1$ is 5

$8 \div 1$ is 8

$20 \div 1$ is 20

$90 \div 1$ is 90

(Chorus 1)

$6 \div 1$ is 6

$9 \div 1$ is 9

$30 \div 1$ is 30

$80 \div 1$ is 80

Any number, I mean any number–
it could be any number at all–
any number divided by one
is that same number.
(Repeat)

$49 \div 1$ is 49

$572 \div 1$ is 572

$1{,}263 \div 1$ is 1,263

$367{,}241 \div 1$ is 367,241

(Chorus 2:)
Any number at all,
could be big or small,
could be a four- or five-
digit number,
for the only thing to remember
is that any number divided by one
is that same number.

Any number divided by one
is that same number.

Any number divided by one
is that same number

Try These

$4{,}243 \div 1$ is

$260{,}122 \div 1$ is

$1{,}369{,}843 \div 1$ is

GREAT!

It Always Equals One

One, one, oh, how fun.
It always equals one.
One, one, oh, how fun.
Now we've only just begun
to learn the different strategies
that will help us to divide.
Like, any number divided by itself
always equals ONE!

One, one, oh, how fun.
It always equals one.
One, one, oh, how fun.
Let me show you how it's done.

$2 \div 2$ is 1

$8 \div 8$ is 1

$12 \div 12$ is 1

$5 \div 5$ is 1

Any number divided by itself
always equals ONE!

(Chorus)

$6 \div 6$ is 1

$3 \div 3$ is 1

$10 \div 10$ is 1

$4 \div 4$ is 1

Any number divided by itself
always equals ONE!

(Chorus)

0 Dividend, Dividing by 1, Same Number

Divide the numbers. Write each quotient.

$5 \div 5 = 1$ $5 \div 1 = 5$ $7 \div 7 = 1$ $9 \div 9 = 1$

$9 \div 1 = 9$ $4 \div 4 = 1$ $3 \div 1 = 3$ $8 \div 8 = 1$

$0 \div 6 = 0$ $3 \div 3 = 1$ $1 \div 1 = 1$ $12 \div 12 = 1$

$90 \div 1 = 90$ $30 \div 30 = 1$ $100 \div 1 = 100$ $40 \div 40 = 1$

$927 \div 1 = 927$ $80 \div 80 = 1$ $20 \div 1 = 20$ $0 \div 1 = 0$

$263 \div 1 = 263$ $263 \div 263 = 1$ $572 \div 1 = 572$ $49 \div 49 = 1$

$16 \div 16 = 1$ $3 \div 3 = 1$ $1215 \div 1 = 1215$ $300 \div 1 = 300$

$29 \div 1 = 29$ $148 \div 1 = 148$ $0 \div 181 = 0$ $21 \div 21 = 1$

$889 \div 889 = 1$ $916 \div 916 = 1$ $1495 \div 1 = 1495$ $1 \div 1 = 1$

$17 \div 1 = 17$ $0 \div 25 = 0$ $25 \div 1 = 25$ $13 \div 1 = 13$

0 Dividend, Dividing by 1, Same Number

Divide the numbers. Write each quotient.

$655 \div 655 = 1$ $701 \div 1 = 701$ $0 \div 83 = 0$ $29 \div 1 = 29$

$655 \div 1 = 655$ $701 \div 701 = 1$ $83 \div 1 = 83$ $0 \div 29 = 0$

$0 \div 655 = 0$ $0 \div 701 = 0$ $83 \div 83 = 1$ $29 \div 29 = 1$

$75 \div 1 = 75$ $444 \div 444 = 1$ $199 \div 1 = 199$ $301 \div 301 = 1$

$0 \div 75 = 0$ $444 \div 1 = 444$ $0 \div 199 = 0$ $301 \div 1 = 301$

$75 \div 75 = 1$ $0 \div 444 = 0$ $7,895 \div 1 = 7895$ $0 \div 301 = 0$

$15 \div 15 = 1$ $0 \div 999 = 0$ $7,895 \div 7,895 = 1$ $0 \div 550 = 0$

$0 \div 15 = 0$ $999 \div 1 = 999$ $0 \div 7,895 = 0$ $550 \div 1 = 550$

$15 \div 1 = 15$ $999 \div 999 = 1$ $1495 \div 1 = 1495$ $550 \div 550 = 1$

$17 \div 1 = 17$ $25 \div 25 = 1$ $25 \div 1 = 25$ $13 \div 1 = 13$

#5 Just Cut It In Half

If you're dividing by two,
I think you should know,
just cut it in half
and the answer will unfold.
Think "half of that number".
It's an easy thing
to figure out the answer.
Now it's time to sing.

Just cut it in half.
Think "half of that number."
Just cut it in half
and you will remember.
Anytime you divide by the number two,
think "half of that number"
and the answer will come to you.

Let's play a fun game. I'll say a number and you tell me what half of that number is. Are you ready?

10	*half is 5*	10 ÷ 2 is 5
12	*half is 6*	12 ÷ 2 is 6
8	*half is 4*	8 ÷ 2 is 4
16	*half is 8*	16 ÷ 2 is 8

(Chorus)

4	*half is 2*	4 ÷ 2 is 2
18	*half is 9*	18 ÷ 2 is 9
6	*half is 3*	6 ÷ 2 is 3
14	*half is 7*	14 ÷ 2 is 7

(Chorus)

Dividing By 2

The facts that you should know about dividing by 2 are:

$0 \div 2 = 0$	$2 \div 2 = 1$	$4 \div 2 = 2$	$6 \div 2 = 3$	$8 \div 2 = 4$
$10 \div 2 = 5$	$12 \div 2 = 6$	$14 \div 2 = 7$	$16 \div 2 = 8$	$18 \div 2 = 9$

Count the objects in each set to determine the **dividend.** Circle groups of 2.
Count The number of groups to determine the **quotient.**

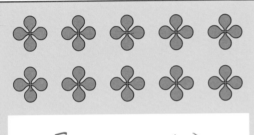

$5 \times 2 = 10$

$4 \times \overset{3}{2} = 12$

$14 \times \overset{1}{2} = 14$

$6 \times \overset{3}{2} = 18$

$6 \times 2 = 6$

$4 \times 2 = 8$

$8 \times 2 = 16$

Division Facts of 2

Write the missing dividend, divisor or quotient.

$2 \div \underline{1} = 2$ $14 \div \underline{7} = 2$ $10 \div \underline{5} = 2$ $12 \div \underline{6} = 2$

$18 \div \underline{2} = 9$ $18 \div \underline{9} = 2$ $8 \div \underline{4} = 2$ $6 \div \underline{2} = 3$

$10 \div \underline{2} = 5$ $2 \div 2 = \underline{1}$ $16 \div 2 = \underline{8}$ $4 \div 2 = \underline{2}$

$12 \div \underline{2} = 6$ $4 \div 2 = \underline{2}$ $14 \div 2 = \underline{7}$ $6 \div 2 = \underline{2}$

$2\overline{)6}^{\,3}$ $\underline{2}\overline{)6}^{\,3}$ $2\overline{)14}^{\,2}$ $2\overline{)8}^{\,4}$ $2\overline{)18}^{\,9}$

$2\overline{)1}^{\,2}$ $2\overline{)12}^{\,24}$ $5\overline{)10}^{\,2}$ $2\overline{)16}^{\,8}$ $2\overline{)2}^{\,2}$

$2\overline{)10}^{\,5}$ $2\overline{)16}^{\,8}$ $7\overline{)14}^{\,2}$ $2\overline{)8}^{\,4}$ $9\overline{)18}^{\,2}$

We're part of the same family–the family of facts.
I'll give you some examples and we will do the math.
We all work together–a mathematical machine.
For when we divide or multiply we make a great team!

Take the numbers 8 and 4 and then the number 2.
Listen as I teach you just what these numbers can do.
8 ÷ 4 is 2 and 4 x 2 is 8 and 8 ÷ 2 is 4.
Do you see how these numbers relate?
So, 2 x 4 is 8. You can divide or multiply.
For we are in the same family–on that you can rely.

*Did you know with three special numbers you can make up two multiplication facts and two division facts? These facts are called a **fact family**. Look at the numbers 10, 2, and 5. 10 ÷ 2 is 5 and 2 x 5 is 10 and 10 ÷ 5 is 2 and 5 x 2 is 10. Do you understand how these numbers are related?*

(Chorus)

Take the numbers 12 and 6 and then the number 2.
Listen as I teach you just what these numbers can do.
12 ÷ 6 is 2 and 6 x 2 is 12 and 12 ÷ 2 is 6.
Now you are starting to delve.
So, 2 x 6 is 12. You can divide or multiply.
For we are in the same family–on that you can rely.

(Chorus)

More Fact Families

Write two multiplication sentences and two division sentences with each set of numbers.

10, 5, 2

____ x ____ = ____   ____ x ____ = ____

____ ÷ ____ = ____   ____ ÷ ____ = ____

6, 3, 18

____ x ____ = ____   ____ x ____ = ____

____ ÷ ____ = ____   ____ ÷ ____ = ____

7, 4, 28

____ x ____ = ____   ____ x ____ = ____

____ ÷ ____ = ____   ____ ÷ ____ = ____

2, 9, 18

____ x ____ = ____   ____ x ____ = ____

____ ÷ ____ = ____   ____ ÷ ____ = ____

Determine the missing number. Write two multiplication sentences and two division sentences with each fact family.

8, 7, ____

____ x ____ = ____   ____ x ____ = ____

____ ÷ ____ = ____   ____ ÷ ____ = ____

3, 8, ____

____ x ____ = ____   ____ x ____ = ____

____ ÷ ____ = ____   ____ ÷ ____ = ____

5, 6, ____

____ x ____ = ____   ____ x ____ = ____

____ ÷ ____ = ____   ____ ÷ ____ = ____

3, 4, ____

____ x ____ = ____   ____ x ____ = ____

____ ÷ ____ = ____   ____ ÷ ____ = ____

7, 2, ____

____ x ____ = ____   ____ x ____ = ____

____ ÷ ____ = ____   ____ ÷ ____ = ____

4, 5, ____

____ x ____ = ____   ____ x ____ = ____

____ ÷ ____ = ____   ____ ÷ ____ = ____

Dividing by 1, Same Number, 2

Write the missing **dividend**, **divisor**, or **quotient**.

WHY DID THE TURKEY CROSS THE ROAD?

Letter Key

T = 6	O = 0	P = 7	I = 18	E = 2	R = 9	V = 3
H = 5	W = 4	S = 10	A = 8	N = 1	C = 12	K = 14

12 ÷ 2 = 6   0 ÷ 5 = 0

   T   O

14 ÷ 2 = 7   9 ÷ 1 = 9   0 ÷ 12 = 0   6 ÷ 2 = 3   10 ÷ 5 = 2

  P   R   O   V   E

5 ÷ 1 = 5   4 ÷ 2 = 2

  H   E

8 ÷ 2 = 4   16 ÷ 2 = 8   10 ÷ 1 = 10   7 ÷ 7 = 1 ,   6 ÷ 2 = 3

  W   A   S   N   T

12 ÷ 1 = 12   5 ÷ 1 = 5   18 ÷ 1 = 18   12 ÷ 1 = 12   14 ÷ 2 = 7   4 ÷ 2 = 2   80 ÷ 80 = 1

  C   H   i   C   K   E   N

Answer: To prove he wasn't chicken

We're Learning To Divide & Multiply

(Chorus 1:)
We're learning to divide and multiply.
We'll say each fact a couple of times
'cause practice makes learning easy & fun.
It will make you smarter when we are done.

(Chorus 2:)
We're learning the facts where the answer is a 2.
We're learning our facts; there are quite a few.
So listen and sing and shout the facts.
It's division and multiplication math.

2 ÷ 1 is 2	2 x 1 is 2	14 ÷ 7 is 2	2 x 7 is 14
4 ÷ 2 is 2	2 x 2 is 4	16 ÷ 8 is 2	2 x 8 is 16
6 ÷ 3 is 2	2 x 3 is 6	18 ÷ 9 is 2	2 x 9 is 18

Now say them once again.   *You're doing great. One more time.*

2 ÷ 1 is 2	2 x 1 is 2	14 ÷ 7 is 2	2 x 7 is 14
4 ÷ 2 is 2	2 x 2 is 4	16 ÷ 8 is 2	2 x 8 is 16
6 ÷ 3 is 2	2 x 3 is 6	18 ÷ 9 is 2	2 x 9 is 18

(Chorus 1)   **(Chorus 1 & 2)**

8 ÷ 4 is 2	2 x 4 is 8
10 ÷ 5 is 2	2 x 5 is 10
12 ÷ 6 is 2	2 x 6 is 12

Now say them one more time.

8 ÷ 4 is 2	2 x 4 is 8
10 ÷ 5 is 2	2 x 5 is 10
12 ÷ 6 is 2	2 x 6 is 12

(Chorus 2)

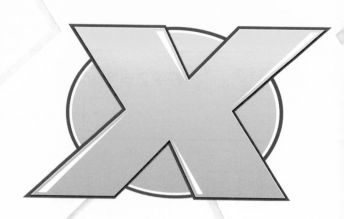

Division and Multiplication

Fill in the missing **quotient**.

$9 \times 8 = 72$ $72 \div 8 = \underline{}$	$6 \times 2 = 12$ $12 \div 6 = \underline{}$	$4 \times 1 = 4$ $4 \div 4 = \underline{}$	$8 \times 5 = 40$ $40 \div 5 = \underline{}$
$3 \times 9 = 27$ $27 \div 3 = \underline{}$	$5 \times 3 = 15$ $15 \div 3 = \underline{}$	$10 \times 6 = 60$ $60 \div 6 = \underline{}$	$2 \times 7 = 14$ $14 \div 2 = \underline{}$
$7 \times 4 = 28$ $28 \div 7 = \underline{}$	$1 \times 10 = 10$ $10 \div 10 = \underline{}$	$10 \times 6 = 60$ $60 \div 10 = \underline{}$	$6 \times 8 = 48$ $48 \div 8 = \underline{}$
$7 \times 7 = 49$ $49 \div 7 = \underline{}$	$1 \times 3 = 3$ $3 \div 3 = \underline{}$	$8 \times 4 = 32$ $32 \div 8 = \underline{}$	$4 \times 10 = 40$ $40 \div 4 = \underline{}$
$9 \times 1 = 9$ $9 \div 1 = \underline{}$	$3 \times 2 = 6$ $6 \div 3 = \underline{}$	$5 \times 5 = 25$ $25 \div 5 = \underline{}$	$2 \times 9 = 18$ $18 \div 9 = \underline{}$
$5 \times 4 = 20$ $20 \div 5 = \underline{}$	$3 \times 7 = 21$ $21 \div 3 = \underline{}$	$1 \times 2 = 2$ $2 \div 2 = \underline{}$	$2 \times 10 = 20$ $20 \div 10 = \underline{}$
$8 \times 1 = 8$ $8 \div 1 = \underline{}$	$9 \times 8 = 72$ $72 \div 9 = \underline{}$	$10 \times 5 = 50$ $50 \div 5 = \underline{}$	$4 \times 3 = 12$ $12 \div 4 = \underline{}$

Division and Multiplication Table

Until you've learned the division facts, a multiplication chart can be used to find any basic division fact. Read down the columns and across the rows. For example, to find the **quotient** to 28 ÷ 7 move one finger down the **Divisor** column 7, stop on the number 28—the **dividend**—then move your finger left all the way to the **Quotient** column, which is 4. (28 ÷ 7 = 4)

Divisor

Quotient	1	2	3	4	5	6	7	8	9	10	11	12
1	1	2	3	4	5	6	7	8	9	10	11	12
2	2	4	6	8	10	12	14	16	18	20	22	24
3	3	6	9	12	15	18	21	24	27	30	33	36
4	4	8	12	16	20	24	28	32	36	40	44	48
5	5	10	15	20	25	30	35	40	45	50	55	60
6	6	12	18	24	30	36	42	48	54	60	66	72
7	7	14	21	28	35	42	49	56	63	70	77	84
8	8	16	24	32	40	48	56	64	72	80	88	96
9	9	18	27	36	45	54	63	72	81	90	99	108
10	10	20	30	40	50	60	70	80	90	100	110	120
11	11	22	33	44	55	66	77	88	99	110	121	132
12	12	24	36	48	60	72	84	96	108	120	132	144

Don't You Agree?

Don't you agree?
Don't you agree?
Don't you agree that the answer is 3?
We'll practice our facts in groups of 3.
Now listen and shout each one with me.

3 ÷ 1 is 3   3 x 1 is 3
6 ÷ 2 is 3   3 x 2 is 6
9 ÷ 3 is 3   3 x 3 is 9

Now let's repeat each fact
just one more time.

3 ÷ 1 is 3   3 x 1 is 3
6 ÷ 2 is 3   3 x 2 is 6
9 ÷ 3 is 3   3 x 3 is 9

(Chorus)

12 ÷ 4 is 3   3 x 4 is 12
15 ÷ 5 is 3   3 x 5 is 15
18 ÷ 6 is 3   3 x 6 is 18

Let's repeat each fact
just one more time.

12 ÷ 4 is 3   3 x 4 is 12
15 ÷ 5 is 3   3 x 5 is 15
18 ÷ 6 is 3   3 x 6 is 18

(Chorus)

21 ÷ 7 is 3   3 x 7 is 21
24 ÷ 8 is 3   3 x 8 is 24
27 ÷ 9 is 3   3 x 9 is 27

Let's repeat each fact
just one more time.

21 ÷ 7 is 3   3 x 7 is 21
24 ÷ 8 is 3   3 x 8 is 24
27 ÷ 9 is 3   3 x 9 is 27

Don't you agree that the answer is three?
Don't you agree that practice is the key?
Don't you agree? We have learned our facts!
It's the only cool way to study math.

Facts of 3

The facts that you should know about dividing by three are:

$0 \div 3 = 0$	$3 \div 3 = 1$	$6 \div 3 = 2$	$9 \div 3 = 3$	$12 \div 3 = 4$
$15 \div 3 = 5$	$18 \div 3 = 6$	$21 \div 3 = 7$	$24 \div 3 = 8$	$27 \div 3 = 9$

Rewrite each division fact of 3 so that the **quotient** equals 3. One fact has been done for you. Do you know which fact of three cannot be rewritten!

Fact of Three:	Rewrite:
$3 \div 3 = 1$	$3 \div 1 = 3$

- Count the objects in each set to determine the **dividend**.
- Circle groups of 3
- Count the number of groups to determine the **quotient**

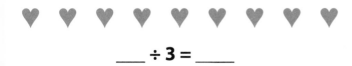

___ ÷ 3 = ____

♦ ♦ ♦ ♦ ♦ ♦ ♦ ♦ ♦ ♦ ♦ ♦

___ ÷ 3 = ____

◎ ◎

___ ÷ 3 = ____

___ ÷ 3 = ____

■ ■ ■ ■ ■ ■ ■ ■ ■ ■ ■ ■ ■ ■ ■ ■ ■ ■

___ ÷ 3 = ____

___ ÷ 3 = ____

Division Facts of 3

Write the missing **dividend**, **divisor** or **quotient**.

$3 \div \underline{\hphantom{0}} = 3$ $12 \div \underline{\hphantom{0}} = 3$ $15 \div \underline{\hphantom{0}} = 3$ $27 \div \underline{\hphantom{0}} = 9$

$18 \div \underline{\hphantom{0}} = 3$ $21 \div \underline{\hphantom{0}} = 7$ $6 \div \underline{\hphantom{0}} = 2$ $9 \div \underline{\hphantom{0}} = 3$

$24 \div \underline{\hphantom{0}} = 3$ $27 \div 3 = \underline{\hphantom{0}}$ $3 \div 3 = \underline{\hphantom{0}}$ $18 \div 6 = \underline{\hphantom{0}}$

$12 \div \underline{\hphantom{0}} = 4$ $15 \div 3 = \underline{\hphantom{0}}$ $24 \div 8 = \underline{\hphantom{0}}$ $21 \div 3 = \underline{\hphantom{0}}$

$2 \overline{)6}$ $\overset{3}{\underline{\hphantom{0}}\overline{)18}}$ $3 \overline{)15}$ $3 \overline{)9}$ $3 \overline{)18}$

$\overset{3}{5 \overline{)\underline{\hphantom{0}}}}$ $3 \overline{)12}$ $\overset{3}{\underline{\hphantom{0}}\overline{)27}}$ $\overset{8}{3 \overline{)\underline{\hphantom{0}}}}$ $3 \overline{)3}$

$7 \overline{)21}$ $5 \overline{)15}$ $\overset{3}{\underline{\hphantom{0}}\overline{)24}}$ $\overset{3}{\underline{\hphantom{0}}\overline{)9}}$ $\overset{6}{\underline{\hphantom{0}}\overline{)18}}$

Facts of 2, 3 Cross-Number Puzzler

Fill the division sentences and
quotients into the puzzle.

Across

2. $18 \div 2 =$
3. $0 \div 2 =$
5. $8 \div 2 =$
6. $12 \div 3 =$
7. $18 \div 3 =$
9. $14 \div 2 =$
10. $6 \div 2 =$
11. $9 \div 3 =$
13. $21 \div 3 =$
15. $27 \div 3 =$
16. $3 \div 3 =$

Down

1. $2 \div 2 =$
2. $16 \div 2 =$
3. $0 \div 3 =$
4. $24 \div 3 =$
6. $10 \div 2 =$
8. $6 \div 3 =$
9. $15 \div 3 =$
12. $4 \div 2 =$
14. $12 \div 2 =$

Let's Explore The Facts Of Four

Let's explore the facts of four.
We'll divide and multiply
with a catchy rhythm and
a rhyme or two.
I will gladly be your guide.

I will say each division fact
then I want you to reply
with a multiplication fact.
Are you ready to have a good time?

4 ÷ 1 is 4	4 x 1 is 4
8 ÷ 2 is 4	4 x 2 is 8
12 ÷ 3 is 4	4 x 3 is 12

Let's explore the facts of four.
Are you ready to learn some more?

16 ÷ 4 is 4	4 x 4 is 16
20 ÷ 5 is 4	4 x 5 is 20
24 ÷ 6 is 4	4 x 6 is 24

Let's explore the facts of four
so, on your test, an "A" you'll score.

28 ÷ 7 is 4	4 x 7 is 28
32 ÷ 8 is 4	4 x 8 is 32
36 ÷ 9 is 4	4 x 9 is 36

(Chorus)

I will say each division fact
then I want you to reply
with a multiplication fact.
Are you ready to have a good time?

4 ÷ 1 is 4	4 x 1 is 4
8 ÷ 2 is 4	4 x 2 is 8
12 ÷ 3 is 4	4 x 3 is 12
16 ÷ 4 is 4	4 x 4 is 16
20 ÷ 5 is 4	4 x 5 is 20
24 ÷ 6 is 4	4 x 6 is 24
28 ÷ 7 is 4	4 x 7 is 28
32 ÷ 8 is 4	4 x 8 is 32
36 ÷ 9 is 4	4 x 9 is 36

We explored the facts of four.
We explored the facts of four.
We explored the facts of four.
So, on our tests, an "A" we'll score!

- Find the **sum**.
- Count the number of **addends**.
- Fill in the missing **dividend** and **quotient**.

4 + 4 + 4 = _____

_____ groups of the number _____   _____ ÷ 4 = _____

4 + 4 + 4 + 4 + 4 = _____

_____ groups of the number _____   _____ ÷ 4 = _____

4 + 4 + 4 + 4 + 4 + 4 + 4 = _____

_____ groups of the number _____   _____ ÷ 4 = _____

4 + 4 + 4 + 4 + 4 + 4 + 4 + 4 = _____

_____ groups of the number _____   _____ ÷ 4 = _____

4 + 4 = _____

_____ groups of the number _____   _____ ÷ 4 = _____

4 + 4 + 4 + 4 + 4 + 4 = _____

_____ groups of the number _____   _____ ÷ 4 = _____

4 + 4 + 4 + 4 + 4 + 4 + 4 + 4 + 4 = _____

_____ groups of the number _____   _____ ÷ 4 = _____

4 + 4 + 4 + 4 = _____

_____ groups of the number _____   _____ ÷ 4 = _____

Division Facts of 4

Write the missing **dividend, divisor** or **quotient.**

$4 \div \underline{\quad} = 1$ $12 \div \underline{\quad} = 3$ $16 \div \underline{\quad} = 4$ $28 \div \underline{\quad} = 4$

$20 \div \underline{\quad} = 4$ $24 \div \underline{\quad} = 6$ $8 \div \underline{\quad} = 2$ $12 \div \underline{\quad} = 4$

$24 \div \underline{\quad} = 4$ $28 \div 4 = \underline{\quad}$ $20 \div 5 = \underline{\quad}$ $16 \div 4 = \underline{\quad}$

$12 \div \underline{\quad} = 4$ $36 \div 4 = \underline{\quad}$ $24 \div 4 = \underline{\quad}$ $32 \div 8 = \underline{\quad}$

$\underline{\quad}\overline{)36}^{\,9}$ $\underline{\quad}\overline{)16}^{\,4}$ $4\overline{)28}$ $5\overline{)20}$ $4\overline{)32}$

$4\overline{)\underline{\quad}}^{\,3}$ $3\overline{)12}$ $\underline{\quad}\overline{)8}^{\,4}$ $4\overline{)\underline{\quad}}^{\,8}$ $4\overline{)36}$

$7\overline{)28}$ $4\overline{)20}$ $\underline{\quad}\overline{)24}^{\,4}$ $\underline{\quad}\overline{)36}^{\,4}$ $\underline{\quad}\overline{)12}^{\,3}$

Hey, Do You Know?

Hey, do you know the facts of five?
Can you say each fact, one at a time?
Now say them in rhythm, kind of slow,
and soon the facts of 5 you'll know.

Hey, hey, do you know?
Hey, do you know just how it goes?
Like counting by 5s—you know the drill.
It takes the ultimate mathematical skill.

5 ÷ 1 is 5   5 x 1 is 5
10 ÷ 2 is 5   5 x 2 is 10
15 ÷ 3 is 5   5 x 3 is 15

Now, one more time, the division line.

5 ÷ 1 is 5
10 ÷ 2 is 5
15 ÷ 3 is 5

We're learning our fives. My, oh my!

(Chorus)

20 ÷ 4 is 5   5 x 4 is 20
25 ÷ 5 is 5   5 x 5 is 25
30 ÷ 6 is 5   5 x 6 is 30

Now, one more time, the division line.

20 ÷ 4 is 5
25 ÷ 5 is 5
30 ÷ 6 is 5

We're learning our fives. My, oh my!

(Chorus)

35 ÷ 7 is 5   5 x 7 is 35
40 ÷ 8 is 5   5 x 8 is 40
45 ÷ 9 is 5   5 x 9 is 45

Now, one more time, the division line.

35 ÷ 7 is 5
40 ÷ 8 is 5
45 ÷ 9 is 5

We're learning our fives. My, oh my!

(Chorus)

Facts of 5

The facts that you should know about dividing by five are:

$0 \div 5 = 0$	$5 \div 5 = 1$	$10 \div 5 = 2$	$15 \div 5 = 3$	$20 \div 5 = 4$
$25 \div 5 = 5$	$30 \div 5 = 6$	$35 \div 5 = 7$	$40 \div 5 = 8$	$45 \div 5 = 9$

Write each fact of 5 with a colored pencil. Trace each fact of five with a different colored pencil. Repeat five times with different colors!

Division Facts of 5

Write the missing dividend, divisor or quotient.

$5 \div \underline{\quad} = 1$ $\qquad$ $15 \div \underline{\quad} = 3$ $\qquad$ $20 \div \underline{\quad} = 4$ $\qquad$ $30 \div \underline{\quad} = 6$

$20 \div \underline{\quad} = 5$ $\qquad$ $45 \div \underline{\quad} = 5$ $\qquad$ $40 \div \underline{\quad} = 8$ $\qquad$ $15 \div \underline{\quad} = 5$

$35 \div \underline{\quad} = 5$ $\qquad$ $5 \div 5 = \underline{\quad}$ $\qquad$ $20 \div 5 = \underline{\quad}$ $\qquad$ $45 \div 9 = \underline{\quad}$

$40 \div \underline{\quad} = 5$ $\qquad$ $35 \div 5 = \underline{\quad}$ $\qquad$ $30 \div 6 = \underline{\quad}$ $\qquad$ $15 \div 5 = \underline{\quad}$

$\underline{\quad}\overline{)45}$ quotient 9 $\qquad$ $\underline{\quad}\overline{)20}$ quotient 4 $\qquad$ $7\overline{)35}$ $\qquad$ $5\overline{)20}$ $\qquad$ $5\overline{)40}$

$5\overline{)\underline{\quad}}$ quotient 3 $\qquad$ $5\overline{)30}$ $\qquad$ $\underline{\quad}\overline{)40}$ quotient 5 $\qquad$ $9\overline{)\underline{\quad}}$ quotient 5 $\qquad$ $5\overline{)25}$

$2\overline{)10}$ $\qquad$ $4\overline{)20}$ $\qquad$ $\underline{\quad}\overline{)35}$ quotient 5 $\qquad$ $\underline{\quad}\overline{)15}$ quotient 5 $\qquad$ $\underline{\quad}\overline{)45}$ quotient 9

Facts of 2, 3, 4, 5

Fill in the missing dividend, divisor or quotient to complete each division sentence

$10 \div 2 = \underline{\quad}$ $\underline{\quad} \div 5 = 7$ $24 \div \underline{\quad} = 6$ $12 \div \underline{\quad} = 3$

$36 \div \underline{\quad} = 9$ $\underline{\quad} \div 4 = 3$ $24 \div \underline{\quad} = 8$ $18 \div \underline{\quad} = 9$

$14 \div \underline{\quad} = 7$ $18 \div \underline{\quad} = 6$ $28 \div \underline{\quad} = 7$ $\underline{\quad} \div 5 = 9$

$20 \div \underline{\quad} = 4$ $12 \div 2 = \underline{\quad}$ $18 \div \underline{\quad} = 9$ $32 \div \underline{\quad} = 8$

$21 \div \underline{\quad} = 7$ $40 \div \underline{\quad} = 8$ $20 \div \underline{\quad} = 10$ $\underline{\quad} \div 5 = 2$

$12 \div \underline{\quad} = 4$ $30 \div \underline{\quad} = 6$ $36 \div \underline{\quad} = 9$ $24 \div \underline{\quad} = 6$

$16 \div \underline{\quad} = 8$ $14 \div 2 = \underline{\quad}$ $28 \div \underline{\quad} = 7$ $18 \div 2 = \underline{\quad}$

$32 \div \underline{\quad} = 8$ $25 \div \underline{\quad} = 5$ $\underline{\quad} \div 5 = 6$ $40 \div \underline{\quad} = 10$

$\underline{\quad} \div 5 = 9$ $24 \div \underline{\quad} = 6$ $16 \div \underline{\quad} = 8$ $35 \div \underline{\quad} = 7$

$40 \div 5 = \underline{\quad}$ $\underline{\quad} \div 5 = 3$ $32 \div \underline{\quad} = 8$ $12 \div \underline{\quad} = 3$

$45 \div \underline{\quad} = 9$ $21 \div 3 = \underline{\quad}$ $15 \div \underline{\quad} = 3$ $\underline{\quad} \div 5 = 5$

$\underline{\quad} \div 4 = 4$ $18 \div \underline{\quad} = 6$ $\underline{\quad} \div 4 = 9$ $16 \div \underline{\quad} = 8$

It's The Only Way

It's the only way.
It's the only way.
It's the only way to learn.
Repetition is the only way.

(Repeat)

Say them once.
Say them twice.
Say them over again.
Say them fast.
Say them slow.
Get them in your head.

Let's divide and multiply.
Now echo after me.
I'll say them first and you repeat
each fact right after me.

6 ÷ 1 is 6   6 x 1 is 6
 (6 ÷ 1 is 6   6 x 1 is 6)

12 ÷ 2 is 6   6 x 2 is 12
(12 ÷ 2 is 6   6 x 2 is 12)

18 ÷ 3 is 6   6 x 3 is 18
(18 ÷ 3 is 6   6 x 3 is 18)

(Chorus)

24 ÷ 4 is 6   6 x 4 is 24
(24 ÷ 4 is 6   6 x 4 is 24)

30 ÷ 5 is 6   6 x 5 is 30
(30 ÷ 5 is 6   6 x 5 is 30)

36 ÷ 6 is 6   6 x 6 is 36
(36 ÷ 6 is 6   6 x 6 is 36)

(Chorus)

Say them once.
Say them twice.
Say them over again.
Say them fast.
Say them slow.
Get them in your head.

42 ÷ 7 is 6   6 x 7 is 42
(42 ÷ 7 is 6   6 x 7 is 42)

48 ÷ 8 is 6   6 x 8 is 48
(48 ÷ 8 is 6   6 x 8 is 48)

54 ÷ 9 is 6   6 x 9 is 54
(54 ÷ 9 is 6   6 x 9 is 54)

(Chorus 2x)

Division Facts of 6

The division facts of six are:

$0 \div 6 = 0$	$6 \div 6 = 1$	$12 \div 6 = 2$	$18 \div 6 = 3$	$24 \div 6 = 4$
$30 \div 6 = 5$	$36 \div 6 = 6$	$42 \div 6 = 7$	$48 \div 6 = 8$	$54 \div 6 = 9$

Find and circle each division fact of 6. The facts may be horizontal or vertical.

48	0	0	18	42	54	12	6	30	36
÷	36	÷	6	=	6	18	42	=	7
6	÷	6	=	1	12	÷	12	54	30
=	42	=	18	54	=	30	÷	6	0
8	=	0	24	48	42	÷	6	=	7
18	48	12	÷	0	12	6	=	48	54
0	54	÷	6	=	9	=	2	18	42
36	12	6	=	48	54	5	0	÷	18
24	54	42	4	18	18	÷	6	=	3

Division Facts of 6

Write the missing dividend, divisor or quotient.

$6 \div \underline{\quad} = 6$ $18 \div \underline{\quad} = 3$ $24 \div \underline{\quad} = 4$ $42 \div \underline{\quad} = 7$

$54 \div \underline{\quad} = 6$ $12 \div \underline{\quad} = 2$ $30 \div \underline{\quad} = 5$ $48 \div \underline{\quad} = 6$

$30 \div \underline{\quad} = 6$ $24 \div 4 = \underline{\quad}$ $6 \div 6 = \underline{\quad}$ $18 \div 3 = \underline{\quad}$

$48 \div \underline{\quad} = 8$ $36 \div 6 = \underline{\quad}$ $30 \div 6 = \underline{\quad}$ $24 \div 4 = \underline{\quad}$

$\underline{\quad} \overline{)48} \; ^6$ $\underline{\quad} \overline{)18} \; ^6$ $7 \overline{)42}$ $5 \overline{)30}$ $6 \overline{)54}$

$6 \overline{)\underline{\quad}} \; ^6$ $5 \overline{)30}$ $\underline{\quad} \overline{)24} \; ^6$ $6 \overline{)\underline{\quad}} \; ^5$ $6 \overline{)42}$

$2 \overline{)12}$ $4 \overline{)24}$ $\underline{\quad} \overline{)36} \; ^6$ $\underline{\quad} \overline{)18} \; ^3$ $\underline{\quad} \overline{)48} \; ^8$

The Quotient Is Seven

The quotient is seven–it doesn't change.
The quotient is seven–it stays the same.
As we say the facts let's keep in mind
that the quotient is seven every time!

(Repeat)

Every time, every time,
the quotient is seven every time.
Every time, every time,
the quotient is seven every time.

7 ÷ 1 is 7   7 x 1 is 7

14 ÷ 2 is 7   7 x 2 is 14

21 ÷ 3 is 7   7 x 3 is 21

Seven, seven, seven. Just keep in mind
that the quotient is seven every time.

28 ÷ 4 is 7   7 x 4 is 28

35 ÷ 5 is 7   7 x 5 is 35

42 ÷ 6 is 7   7 x 6 is 42

Seven, seven, seven. Just keep in mind
that the quotient is seven every time.

(Chorus)

49 ÷ 7 is 7   7 x 7 is 49

56 ÷ 8 is 7   7 x 8 is 56

63 ÷ 9 is 7   7 x 9 is 63

Seven, seven, seven. Just keep in mind
that the quotient is seven every time.

(Chorus)

The quotient is seven every time.

Division Facts of 7

The division facts of seven are:

$0 \div 7 = 0$ $7 \div 7 = 1$ $14 \div 7 = 2$ $21 \div 7 = 3$ $28 \div 7 = 4$

$35 \div 7 = 5$ $42 \div 7 = 6$ $49 \div 7 = 7$ $56 \div 7 = 8$ $63 \div 7 = 9$

Fill in the chart below with two division sentences
and two multiplication sentences for each fact.

Divisor = 7	Quotient = 7	Multiplication Fact 1	Multiplication Fact 2
$7 \div 7 = 1$	$7 \div 1 = 7$	$7 \times 1 = 7$	$1 \times 7 = 7$

Division Facts of 7

Write the missing **dividend**, **divisor** or **quotient**.

$7 \div \_\_\_ = 1$ $35 \div \_\_\_ = 7$ $28 \div \_\_\_ = 4$ $42 \div \_\_\_ = 7$

$56 \div \_\_\_ = 7$ $14 \div \_\_\_ = 2$ $35 \div \_\_\_ = 5$ $63 \div \_\_\_ = 9$

$49 \div \_\_\_ = 7$ $21 \div 3 = \_\_\_$ $7 \div 7 = \_\_\_$ $56 \div 7 = \_\_\_$

$63 \div \_\_\_ = 7$ $28 \div 4 = \_\_\_$ $21 \div 7 = \_\_\_$ $49 \div 7 = \_\_\_$

$\underline{} \overline{)7} \; ^{7}$ $\underline{} \overline{)28} \; ^{4}$ $7 \overline{)42}$ $5 \overline{)35}$ $6 \overline{)42}$

$7 \overline{)\underline{}} \; ^{9}$ $7 \overline{)21}$ $\underline{} \overline{)56} \; ^{8}$ $6 \overline{)\underline{}} \; ^{7}$ $7 \overline{)63}$

$2 \overline{)14}$ $7 \overline{)49}$ $\underline{} \overline{)28} \; ^{4}$ $\underline{} \overline{)21} \; ^{3}$ $\underline{} \overline{)56} \; ^{7}$

Facts of 2,3,4,5,6,7

- Count the objects in each set to determine the **dividend**.
- Circle the equal groups.
- Count the objects in each group to determine the **quotient**.

Circle groups of 7.

____ ÷ __7__ = ____

Circle groups of 4.

____ ÷ __4__ = ____

Circle groups of 3.

____ ÷ __3__ = ____

Circle groups of 5.

____ ÷ __5__ = ____

Circle groups of 2.

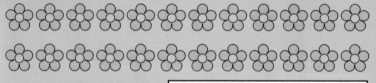

____ ÷ __2__ = ____

Circle groups of 2.

____ ÷ __2__ = ____

Circle groups of 5.

____ ÷ __5__ = ____

Circle 5 equal groups. Can you circle 6 equal groups?

____ ÷ __6__ = ____

____ ÷ __5__ = ____

37

Division FACTS Bingo

Each player will need 25 markers, paper, and a pencil. Players draw the game board 5 columns wide and 6 rows long. Across the top write one letter in each square: F A C T S. Next, each player writes a number 1 through 9 in each of the boxes on his or her game board. Choose a caller. The caller says a division sentence. For example, "F = $36 \div 9$". The players who have the correct quotient in the correct column cover that number with a marker. The first player to completely cover all the numbers in a row, column, or diagonal says "FACTS" and wins the game. The caller should write down all of the calls he or she makes.

F	A	C	T	S
1	5	7	3	9
6	2	9	4	6
4	1	8	5	7
8	3	9	2	5
7	6	4	8	1

Great Lengths

Practice both division and measuring skills with this simple activity. You'll need yarn, a ruler or yardstick, and scissors. Measure and cut a 12-inch length of yarn. Measure and cut that length into 4-inch lengths. How many 4-inch pieces did you cut from the 12-inch length? Say the division sentence this represents. Repeat using other lengths of yarn. For more challenging learning fun, begin with a length that cannot be divided evenly and discover the remainder.

Glass Jar Division

Use glass jars to divide up a child's allowance. Take three glass jars and label them as spending, saving and sharing. When your child gets an allowance, she can split it up and put some money in each jar. That drives home the fact that money isn't just for spending—there's also saving for the future and sharing with others (whether it's for charity or buying gifts for family and friends).

I'm Thinking of a Number

One player secretly writes a number that can divide evenly. Players take turns guessing what number has been written down by asking questions that can be answered "Yes" or "No." For example, player one writes down the number 36. The next player may ask, "Can that number be divided by 6?" Player one answers, "Yes!" The next player may ask, "Can that number be divided by 5?" The first player answers, "No!" On his or her turn, a player may make a guess. If the guess is correct, that player chooses the number for the next round. If the guess is incorrect, play continues. Players may make notes based upon the questions and answers given. Limit the secret numbers to the division facts that you're working with.

I have! Who Has?

On index cards write one quotient and one different division sentence. For example, write 49 and 18 ÷ 3. Deal all the cards out to other players. The first player reads a card. For example, "I have 49. Who has 18 ÷ 3?" The player with a 6 answers, "I have the answer—it's 6," reads the division sentence on his card, and then discards that card. The winner is the first player to discard all the cards in his or her hand.

How Many Numbers Can We Make?

Give each player a piece of paper and a pencil. Remove the face cards from a standard deck of playing cards. Using the cards from 1 to 10, deal four cards out with the numbers showing. Using all four cards and a choice of any combination of addition, subtraction, multiplication, or division, each player makes as many different numbers as possible in 5 minutes. Players get one point for each answer. For example, suppose the cards drawn are 3, 4, 7, and 5. What numbers can be made?

Thumbs Up!

Practice division facts—or multiplication, subtraction, or addition—with this simple activity. One player says a division sentence with a correct or incorrect answer and calls out, "Thumbs up! Thumbs down!" The other players put their thumbs UP if they think the answer is correct, and their thumbs DOWN if they think it is incorrect.

Thumbs Down!

Division Champ

This math learning game is great fun with a large group of friends or an entire classroom. To begin the game, choose two players to stand. Say a division sentence—or any multiplication, subtraction, or addition sentence. Whoever says the correct answer first stays standing. The other player sits down. The next player stands. Continue until only one player is left standing! This person is the Division Champ!

#13

A Little Bit of Music

A little bit of music,
a little bit of soul,
a little bit of rhythm and blues—
I'm told—
will get us on track to investigate
while we memorize
the marvelous facts of eight.

A little bit of music,
a little bit of soul,
and how about a little bit
of rock 'n' roll!
Let's say the marvelous facts of eight
while we jam with the music
as we calculate.

$8 \div 1$ is 8 8×1 is 8

$16 \div 2$ is 8 8×2 is 16

$24 \div 3$ is 8 8×3 is 24

A little bit of music, a little bit of soul,
and a little bit of really cool rock 'n' roll.

$32 \div 4$ is 8 8×4 is 32

$40 \div 5$ is 8 8×5 is 40

$48 \div 6$ is 8 8×6 is 48

A little bit of music, a little bit of soul,
and a little bit of really cool rock 'n' roll.

$56 \div 7$ is 8 8×7 is 56

$64 \div 8$ is 8 8×8 is 64 $64 \div 8 = 8$

$72 \div 9$ is 8 8×9 is 72

(Chorus)

40

Division Facts of 8

Write the missing dividend, divisor or quotient.

$8 \div \underline{\hspace{1cm}} = 1$ $32 \div \underline{\hspace{1cm}} = 4$ $8 \div 8 = \underline{\hspace{1cm}}$

$56 \div \underline{\hspace{1cm}} = 8$ $16 \div 2 = \underline{\hspace{1cm}}$ $48 \div \underline{\hspace{1cm}} = 6$

$24 \div \underline{\hspace{1cm}} = 3$ $64 \div \underline{\hspace{1cm}} = 8$ $72 \div \underline{\hspace{1cm}} = 9$

$56 \div \underline{\hspace{1cm}} = 7$ $40 \div \underline{\hspace{1cm}} = 5$ $56 \div 7 = \underline{\hspace{1cm}}$

$$\underline{\hspace{0.8cm}} \overline{)\,56}^{\,7} \qquad \underline{\hspace{0.8cm}} \overline{)\,32}^{\,4} \qquad 8\overline{)\,64} \qquad 8\overline{)\,72} \qquad 1\overline{)\,8}$$

$$6\overline{)\underline{\hspace{1cm}}}^{\,8} \qquad 5\overline{)\,40} \qquad \underline{\hspace{0.8cm}}\overline{)\,48}^{\,8} \qquad 4\overline{)\underline{\hspace{1cm}}}^{\,8} \qquad 9\overline{)\,72}$$

2-8 Double Dash

How fast will you Double Dash to the center? Practice the division facts 2-8. Say aloud the quotient. Predict how quickly you can move to the center. Set a timer and discover how well you know division facts! Photocopy this page so that you can practice your division facts over and over.

	32 ÷ 8	72 ÷ 8	21 ÷ 7	28 ÷ 4	20 ÷ 5	12 ÷ 6	21 ÷ 3	14 ÷ 7	54 ÷ 6
30 ÷ 6	24 ÷ 4	48 ÷ 6	42 ÷ 7	20 ÷ 5	12 ÷ 2	6 ÷ 3	18 ÷ 2	14 ÷ 7	24 ÷ 8
64 ÷ 8	54 ÷ 6	35 ÷ 7	30 ÷ 6	12 ÷ 4	18 ÷ 3	14 ÷ 2	8 ÷ 4	16 ÷ 4	25 ÷ 5
32 ÷ 4	48 ÷ 8	28 ÷ 4	14 ÷ 7	21 ÷ 3	10 ÷ 2	12 ÷ 4	21 ÷ 7	40 ÷ 5	27 ÷ 3
18 ÷ 3	63 ÷ 7	45 ÷ 5	54 ÷ 6	30 ÷ 5	★	36 ÷ 6	24 ÷ 4	42 ÷ 7	49 ÷ 7
63 ÷ 7	35 ÷ 5	18 ÷ 6	25 ÷ 5	10 ÷ 2	18 ÷ 2	14 ÷ 2	6 ÷ 3	24 ÷ 4	36 ÷ 4
20 ÷ 5	32 ÷ 8	72 ÷ 8	21 ÷ 7	28 ÷ 4	20 ÷ 5	12 ÷ 6	21 ÷ 3	14 ÷ 7	54 ÷ 6
12 ÷ 2	30 ÷ 6	40 ÷ 5	48 ÷ 8	12 ÷ 4	14 ÷ 7	21 ÷ 3	10 ÷ 2	12 ÷ 4	64 ÷ 8
18 ÷ 3	24 ÷ 6	16 ÷ 8	64 ÷ 8	54 ÷ 6	35 ÷ 7	30 ÷ 6	16 ÷ 4	28 ÷ 4	32 ÷ 4
14 ÷ 2	8 ÷ 4	16 ÷ 4	25 ÷ 5	18 ÷ 6	25 ÷ 5	10 ÷ 2	18 ÷ 2	45 ÷ 5	18 ÷ 3
12 ÷ 4	18 ÷ 3	14 ÷ 2	8 ÷ 4	16 ÷ 4	21 ÷ 7	12 ÷ 6	12 ÷ 6	18 ÷ 6	63 ÷ 7
28 ÷ 7	49 ÷ 7	15 ÷ 3	30 ÷ 6	12 ÷ 4	18 ÷ 3	14 ÷ 2	8 ÷ 4	72 ÷ 8	40 ÷ 8

The Fabulous Facts of 9

Let's hear the sax.
Let's hear the drums.
Now the guitar.
We're having fun.

The facts of nine.
The facts of nine.
The fabulous facts of nine. It's time
to divide and multiply the fabulous,
fabulous facts of nine.

9 ÷ 1 is 9	9 x 1 is 9
18 ÷ 2 is 9	9 x 2 is 18
27 ÷ 3 is 9	9 x 3 is 27

You're doing great.
Yeah, you're doing fine!
You're learning the
fabulous facts of nine.

9 ÷ 1 is 9

18 ÷ 2 is 9

27 ÷ 3 is 9

You're doing great.
Yeah, you're doing fine!
You're learning the
fabulous facts of nine.

(Chorus)

36 ÷ 4 is 9	9 x 4 is 36
45 ÷ 5 is 9	9 x 5 is 45
54 ÷ 6 is 9	9 x 6 is 54

You're doing great.
Yeah, you're doing fine!
You're learning the
fabulous facts of nine.

36 ÷ 4 is 9

45 ÷ 5 is 9

54 ÷ 6 is 9

You're doing great.
Yeah, you're doing fine!
You're learning the
fabulous facts of nine.

(Chorus)

63 ÷ 7 is 9	9 x 7 is 63
72 ÷ 8 is 9	9 x 8 is 72
81 ÷ 9 is 9	9 x 9 is 81

You're doing great.
Yeah, you're doing fine!
You're learning the
fabulous facts of nine.

63 ÷ 7 is 9

72 ÷ 8 is 9

81 ÷ 9 is 9

You're doing great.
Yeah, you're doing fine!
You're learning the
fabulous facts of nine.

(Chorus)

Division Facts of 9

The division facts of nine are:

$0 \div 9 = 0$	$9 \div 9 = 1$	$18 \div 9 = 2$	$27 \div 9 = 3$	$36 \div 9 = 4$
$45 \div 9 = 5$	$54 \div 9 = 6$	$63 \div 9 = 7$	$72 \div 9 = 8$	$81 \div 9 = 9$

- Count the objects in each box to determine the **dividend.**
- Circle groups of 9.
- Count the number of groups to determine the **quotient.**

_____ $\div$ __9__ = _____

_____ $\div$ __9__ = _____

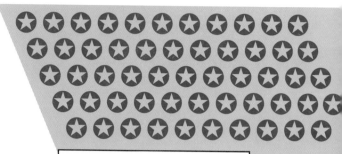

_____ $\div$ __9__ = _____

_____ $\div$ __9__ = _____

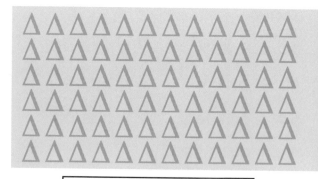

_____ $\div$ __9__ = _____

_____ $\div$ __9__ = _____

44

Division Facts of 9

Write the missing dividend, divisor or quotient.

$9 \div \underline{\quad} = 9$ $\qquad$ $54 \div \underline{\quad} = 6$ $\qquad$ $45 \div \underline{\quad} = 9$ $\qquad$ $63 \div \underline{\quad} = 7$

$54 \div \underline{\quad} = 9$ $\qquad$ $36 \div \underline{\quad} = 4$ $\qquad$ $72 \div \underline{\quad} = 8$ $\qquad$ $18 \div \underline{\quad} = 9$

$27 \div \underline{\quad} = 3$ $\qquad$ $18 \div 2 = \underline{\quad}$ $\qquad$ $9 \div 9 = \underline{\quad}$ $\qquad$ $81 \div 9 = \underline{\quad}$

$72 \div \underline{\quad} = 8$ $\qquad$ $45 \div 9 = \underline{\quad}$ $\qquad$ $63 \div 7 = \underline{\quad}$ $\qquad$ $36 \div 4 = \underline{\quad}$

$\underline{\quad}\overline{)63}$ quotient 7 $\qquad$ $\underline{\quad}\overline{)36}$ quotient 9 $\qquad$ $9\overline{)81}$ $\qquad$ $8\overline{)72}$ $\qquad$ $1\overline{)9}$

$6\overline{)\underline{\quad}}$ quotient 9 $\qquad$ $9\overline{)18}$ $\qquad$ $\underline{\quad}\overline{)45}$ quotient 9 $\qquad$ $4\overline{)\underline{\quad}}$ quotient 9 $\qquad$ $9\overline{)72}$

$7\overline{)63}$ $\qquad$ $9\overline{)27}$ $\qquad$ $\underline{\quad}\overline{)36}$ quotient 4 $\qquad$ $\underline{\quad}\overline{)9}$ quotient 1 $\qquad$ $\underline{\quad}\overline{)81}$ quotient 9

Division Target Practice- Facts of 2,3,4,5,6,7,8,9

Complete the target practice by filling in the missing **DIVISOR** or **DIVIDEND** that equal the **QUOTIENT** in the center. The outer circle is the **DIVIDEND**. The middle circle is the **DIVISOR**.

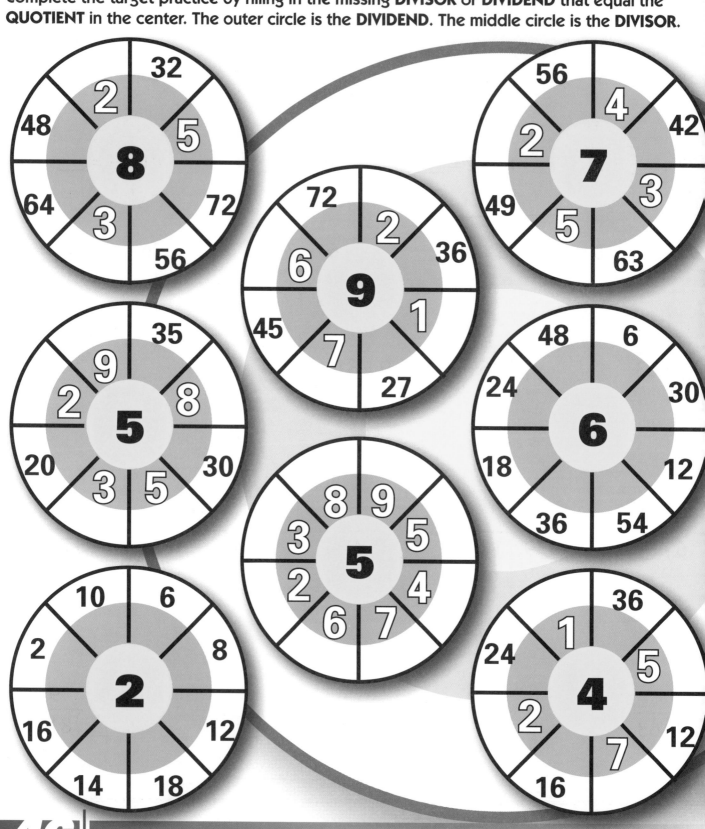

Facts of 2,3,4,5,6,7,8,9

Write the correct **quotient**. Find and circle each division sentence in the puzzle.
Write a ÷ and an = sign in the correct place.

$18 \div 3 =$ ___	$3 \div 3 =$ ___	$6 \div 2 =$ ___	$10 \div 2 =$ ___
$14 \div 2 =$ ___	$24 \div 3 =$ ___	$36 \div 6 =$ ___	$72 \div 8 =$ ___
$49 \div 7 =$ ___	$10 \div 5 =$ ___	$54 \div 9 =$ ___	$12 \div 6 =$ ___
$28 \div 4 =$ ___	$30 \div 5 =$ ___	$16 \div 2 =$ ___	$40 \div 8 =$ ___
$16 \div 4 =$ ___	$27 \div 9 =$ ___	$36 \div 4 =$ ___	$81 \div 9 =$ ___

18 ÷ 3 = 6			40	6	2	3	16	2	8
5	3	12	2	24	3	8	16	6	10
24	1	6	36	4	9	12	6	49	5
72	25	2	35	30	21	36	18	7	2
27	8	54	25	5	36	14	2	7	20
9	10	9	81	6	14	16	56	18	14
3	16	6	9	32	16	4	10	2	5
40	8	5	9	12	28	4	7	21	16

Division Facts of 10

The division facts of ten are:

$0 \div 10 = 0$	$10 \div 10 = 1$	$20 \div 10 = 2$	$30 \div 10 = 3$	$40 \div 10 = 4$
$50 \div 10 = 5$	$60 \div 10 = 6$	$70 \div 10 = 7$	$80 \div 10 = 8$	$90 \div 10 = 9$
$100 \div 10 = 10$	$110 \div 10 = 11$	$120 \div 10 = 12$		

Write the correct **quotient.**

$30 \div 10 =$	$60 \div 10 =$	$80 \div 10 =$	$40 \div 10 =$	$50 \div 10 =$
$90 \div 10 =$	$70 \div 10 =$	$20 \div 10 =$	$10 \div 10 =$	$100 \div 10 =$

Write the missing **dividend, divisor** or **quotient.**

$\underline{})\overline{50}$ quotient 5	$\underline{})\overline{30}$ quotient 10	$\underline{})\overline{80}$ quotient 8	$\underline{})\overline{40}$ quotient 10	$9)\overline{90}$
$\underline{})\overline{120}$ quotient 12	$2)\overline{20}$	$\underline{})\overline{110}$ quotient 11	$10)\overline{}$ quotient 11	$7)\overline{70}$
$10)\overline{100}$	$\underline{})\overline{10}$ quotient 1	$\underline{})\overline{60}$ quotient 10	$\underline{})\overline{30}$ quotient 3	$\underline{})\overline{90}$ quotient 9

Finding the Facts of 10

90 ÷ 10 =	10 ÷ 10 =	40 ÷ 10 =
50 ÷ 10 =	30 ÷ 10 =	120 ÷ 10 =
20 ÷ 10 =	100 ÷ 10 =	110 ÷ 10 =
70 ÷ 10 =	80 ÷ 10 =	60 ÷ 10 =

Find and circle each fact of ten.

+	2	5	8	-	7	0	÷	1	0	=	7	x	3	2
1	1	6	9	1	0	x	2	=	5	6	=	2	1	0
2	3	5	0	÷	1	0	=	5	4	1	0	3	5	6
0	x	7	1	-	2	=	8	1	0	=	9	+	1	0
÷	4	2	3	8	+	1	0	2	x	8	9	1	0	÷
1	4	4	9	1	2	=	7	1	0	÷	1	0	=	1
0	+	4	0	÷	1	0	=	4	2	5	0	9	9	0
=	6	8	÷	7	4	3	+	1	0	-	0	7	4	=
1	5	1	1	x	9	0	7	2	3	4	÷	8	+	6
2	x	1	0	=	4	÷	6	x	5	0	1	8	5	4
6	7	1	=	2	+	1	1	0	÷	1	0	=	1	1
4	+	5	9	=	2	0	7	2	8	1	=	5	5	5
x	3	2	=	8	7	=	5	3	2	=	1	4	0	4
2	x	1	0	+	5	3	8	0	÷	1	0	=	8	9
2	0	÷	1	0	=	2	6	8	1	0	x	8	+	3

Division Facts of 11

The division facts of eleven are:

$0 \div 11 = 0$	$11 \div 11 = 1$	$22 \div 11 = 2$	$33 \div 11 = 3$	$44 \div 11 = 4$
$55 \div 11 = 5$	$66 \div 11 = 6$	$77 \div 11 = 7$	$88 \div 11 = 8$	$99 \div 11 = 9$
$110 \div 11 = 10$	$121 \div 11 = 11$	$132 \div 11 = 12$		

Write the correct **quotient.**

$33 \div 11 =$	$66 \div 11 =$	$55 \div 11 =$	$99 \div 11 =$	$121 \div 11 =$
$11 \div 11 =$	$77 \div 11 =$	$44 \div 11 =$	$110 \div 11 =$	$132 \div 11 =$

Write the missing **dividend, divisor** or **quotient.**

$$\underline{}\,\overline{)\,55}^{\,5} \qquad \underline{}\,\overline{)\,33}^{\,11} \qquad \underline{}\,\overline{)\,88}^{\,8} \qquad \underline{}\,\overline{)\,44}^{\,11} \qquad 11\,\overline{)\,99}$$

$$\underline{}\,\overline{)\,121}^{\,11} \qquad 2\,\overline{)\,22} \qquad \underline{}\,\overline{)\,132}^{\,11} \qquad 6\,\overline{)\,\underline{}}^{\,11} \qquad 11\,\overline{)\,11}$$

$$7\,\overline{)\,77} \qquad \underline{}\,\overline{)\,11}^{\,1} \qquad \underline{}\,\overline{)\,110}^{\,11} \qquad \underline{}\,\overline{)\,55}^{\,11} \qquad \underline{}\,\overline{)\,33}^{\,3}$$

Division Facts of 12

The division facts of twelve are:

$0 \div 12 = 0$	$12 \div 12 = 1$	$24 \div 12 = 2$	$36 \div 12 = 3$	$48 \div 12 = 4$
$60 \div 12 = 5$	$72 \div 12 = 6$	$84 \div 12 = 7$	$96 \div 12 = 8$	$108 \div 12 = 9$
$120 \div 12 = 10$	$132 \div 12 = 11$	$144 \div 12 = 12$		

Write the correct **quotient.**

$72 \div 12 =$	$132 \div 12 =$	$60 \div 12 =$	$24 \div 12 =$	$144 \div 12 =$
$12 \div 12 =$	$36 \div 12 =$	$84 \div 12 =$	$0 \div 12 =$	$96 \div 12 =$

$12 \overline{)48}$	$12 \overline{)108}$	$12 \overline{)24}$	$12 \overline{)60}$	$12 \overline{)84}$
$12 \overline{)0}$	$12 \overline{)72}$	$12 \overline{)120}$	$12 \overline{)12}$	$12 \overline{)144}$
$2 \overline{)24}$	$5 \overline{)60}$	$7 \overline{)84}$	$12 \overline{)72}$	$8 \overline{)96}$
$12 \overline{)144}$	$3 \overline{)36}$	$12 \overline{)48}$	$11 \overline{)132}$	$12 \overline{)84}$

Facts of 10,11,12 Maze

Run the maze following only the paths with the correct quotients.

$132 \div 11 = 11$

$120 \div 10 = 12$

$44 \div 11 = 3$

$99 \div 11 = 9$

$96 \div 12 = 7$

$60 \div 12 = 5$

$72 \div 12 = 5$

$96 \div 12 = 6$

$99 \div 9 = 11$

$12 \div 12 = 2$

$84 \div 12 = 7$

$110 \div 11 = 9$

$11 \div 11 = 1$

$40 \div 10 = 4$

$60 \div 10 = 7$

$132 \div 11 = 12$

$99 \div 11 = 8$

$77 \div 11 = 7$

$48 \div 12 = 4$

START

$10 \div 10 = 1$

$24 \div 12 = 2$

$100 \div 10 = 9$

$22 \div 11 = 3$

$60 \div 12 = 5$

$55 \div 11 = 5$

$60 \div 10 = 6$

$96 \div 12 = 7$

$50 \div 10 = 5$

$108 \div 12 = 5$

$40 \div 10 = 4$

$36 \div 12 = 3$

$70 \div 10 = 6$

$110 \div 11 = 10$

Calculator Race

The object of the game is to beat the calculator! You'll need three players. One player says a division sentence from the game board below. The second player solves the problem with the calculator. The third player solves the problem without a calculator. Player one decides who correctly solved the problem first and places that player's initials in the box. Before playing, you may want to photocopy this page so you can play again and again.

28 ÷ 7 =	32 ÷ 4 =	81 ÷ 9 =	63 ÷ 7 =	12 ÷ 4 =	121 ÷ 11 =	99 ÷ 9 =	24 ÷ 8 =	24 ÷ 8 =	48 ÷ 6 =
64 ÷ 8 =	84 ÷ 12 =	60 ÷ 5 =	572 ÷ 1 =	55 ÷ 11 =	72 ÷ 8 =	45 ÷ 9 =	27 ÷ 3 =	108 ÷ 12 =	36 ÷ 6 =
21 ÷ 7 =	144 ÷ 12 =	42 ÷ 6 =	48 ÷ 12 =	60 ÷ 10 =	72 ÷ 12 =	81 ÷ 9 =	54 ÷ 9 =	28 ÷ 4 =	36 ÷ 9 =
20 ÷ 4 =	5 ÷ 5 =	18 ÷ 2 =	0 ÷ 927 =	32 ÷ 8 =	96 ÷ 12 =	120 ÷ 12 =	22 ÷ 11 =	16 ÷ 8 =	14 ÷ 7 =
49 ÷ 7 =	6 ÷ 3 =	24 ÷ 6 =	42 ÷ 7 =	20 ÷ 5 =	9 ÷ 3 =	572 ÷ 1 =	35 ÷ 7 =	132 ÷ 12 =	10 ÷ 2 =
44 ÷ 4 =	40 ÷ 5 =	56 ÷ 8 =	21 ÷ 3 =	45 ÷ 5 =	110 ÷ 10 =	36 ÷ 4 =	15 ÷ 5 =	12 ÷ 6 =	30 ÷ 5 =
33 ÷ 11 =	80 ÷ 10 =	36 ÷ 12 =	55 ÷ 5 =	4 ÷ 2 =	10 ÷ 10 =	66 ÷ 11 =	0 ÷ 494 =	30 ÷ 1 =	100 ÷ 10 =
16 ÷ 4 =	54 ÷ 6 =	90 ÷ 1 =	50 ÷ 10 =	40 ÷ 8 =	72 ÷ 9 =	30 ÷ 1 =	14 ÷ 2 =	36 ÷ 12 =	66 ÷ 11 =
110 ÷ 11 =	120 ÷ 10 =	33 ÷ 3 =	27 ÷ 3 =	25 ÷ 5 =	30 ÷ 6 =	56 ÷ 7 =	0 ÷ 263 =	80 ÷ 1 =	84 ÷ 12 =
10 ÷ 2 =	40 ÷ 4 =	18 ÷ 9 =	692 ÷ 1 =	32 ÷ 4 =	100 ÷ 1 =	6 ÷ 2 =	1 ÷ 1 =	0 ÷ 685 =	44 ÷ 11 =

Rules of Divisibility

Learning the following rules will help you determine if a larger **dividend** can be divided by a specific **divisor**.

A Number can be divided by	
2 if...	the last digit of the **dividend** is 0, 2, 4, 6 or 8. For example: 336 may be divided by 2 because the last digit–the ones–is 6.
3 if...	the sum of the digits in a **dividend** can be divided by 3. For example: 336: 3+3+6=12; 12 can be divided by 3 so 336 can be divided by 3
4 if...	the number formed by the last two digits of the **dividend** may be divided by 4. For example: 416: the last two digits are 16; 16 can be divided by 4 so 416 can be divided by 4.
5 if...	the last digit of the **dividend** is 0 or 5. For example: 625 can be divided by 5, but 621 cannot!
6 if...	the **dividend** may be divided by both 2 and 3. For example: 756: The ones digit is even so it can be divided by 2 AND the sum of the digits 7+5+6=18 is divisible by 3 so 756 can be divided by 6!
9 if...	the sum of the digits in the **dividend** may be divided by 9. For example: 756: The sum of the digits 7+5+6=18; 18 can be divided by 9 so 756 is divisible by 9.
10 if...	the last digit of the **dividend** is 0. For example: 450: the last digit of the number is 0 so 450 can be divided by 10

Rules of Divisibility

Circle the dividends that can be divided by 2.	550	322	447	898
Draw a line through the dividends that can be divided by 3.	129	474	972	824
Draw a box around the dividends that can be divided by 4.	428	132	615	548
Put an X through the dividends that cannot be divided by 5.	100	126	475	329
Circle the dividends that can be divided by 6.	426	714	917	558
Draw a box around the dividends that can be divided by 9.	261	406	288	540
Draw a line through the dividends that can be divided by 10.	750	440	890	655

Division with Remainders

When you divide a number, you sometimes have some left over. This is called a **remainder**.

For example, let's divide 16 by 5.

Draw 16 dots in this square. Circle the dots in groups of 5.
How many groups of 5 did you circle?
How many dots are left over? _____ This is the **remainder.**

This division sentence may be written like this: $16 \div 5 = 3$ **R1** The R means **remainder**.

Solve the following division problems. If you have difficulty, draw dots and circle the groups on another piece of paper.

$18 \div 7 =$ $13 \div 2 =$ $17 \div 5 =$

$12 \div 8 =$ $23 \div 7 =$ $19 \div 5 =$

$29 \div 5 =$ $28 \div 6 =$ $37 \div 9 =$

Count the objects in each set to determine the **dividend**.
Circle equal groups.
Count the number of groups to determine the **quotient**
Count the number of items left over to determine the **remainder**.

Circle groups of 4.

___ ÷ 4 = ____ R____

Circle groups of 7.

♦ ♦ ♦ ♦ ♦ ♦ ♦ ♦ ♦ ♦ ♦ ♦ ♦ ♦ ♦ ♦ ♦

___ ÷ 7 = ____ R____

Circle groups of 4.

___ ÷ 4 = ____ R____

Circle groups of 5.

✳ ✳ ✳ ✳ ✳ ✳ ✳ ✳ ✳ ✳ ✳ ✳ ✳ ✳ ✳ ✳ ✳ ✳

___ ÷ 5 = ____ R____

Circle groups of 4.

■ ■

___ ÷ 4 = ____ R____

Circle groups of 3.

___ ÷ 3 = ____ R____

Two-digit Numbers with Remainders

When dividing objects or numbers, you sometimes have some left over. This is called a **remainder**.

$$6\overline{)31}$$

Look at the first digit of the dividend (3). It is smaller than 6 so it can't be divided by 6 to produce a whole number. Next take the first two digits of the dividend (31) and determine how many 6's it contains. In this case 31 holds five 6's ($5 \times 6 = 30$). Place the 5 above the division bracket.

$$6\overline{)31}^{\,5}$$

Multiply the 5 by 6 and write the result (30) below the 31 of the dividend.

$$\begin{array}{r} 5 \\ 6\overline{)31} \\ 30 \end{array}$$

Draw a line under the 30. Subtract 30 from 31 ($31 - 30 = 1$).

$$\begin{array}{r} 5 \\ 6\overline{)31} \\ \underline{30} \\ 1 \end{array}$$

The number 1 is called the **remainder**. The **remainder** tells you that there is 1 left over. Write **R1** beside the **quotient**.

$$\begin{array}{r} 5\ \text{R1} \\ 6\overline{)31} \\ \underline{30} \\ 1 \end{array}$$

Division with a Remainder

$9\overline{)37}$	$4\overline{)25}$	$7\overline{)65}$	$9\overline{)38}$
$7\overline{)29}$	$5\overline{)24}$	$9\overline{)83}$	$3\overline{)17}$
$4\overline{)31}$	$6\overline{)37}$	$2\overline{)13}$	$8\overline{)27}$
$8\overline{)36}$	$9\overline{)28}$	$8\overline{)59}$	$7\overline{)65}$
$5\overline{)49}$	$7\overline{)54}$	$8\overline{)65}$	$5\overline{)33}$
$5\overline{)29}$	$9\overline{)56}$	$6\overline{)56}$	$9\overline{)38}$

Division with a Remainder

9$\overline{)64}$ 7$\overline{)25}$ 8$\overline{)75}$ 9$\overline{)29}$

6$\overline{)33}$ 9$\overline{)56}$ 8$\overline{)71}$ 6$\overline{)34}$

8$\overline{)52}$ 5$\overline{)41}$ 8$\overline{)63}$ 9$\overline{)39}$

8$\overline{)45}$ 3$\overline{)16}$ 8$\overline{)22}$ 6$\overline{)14}$

8$\overline{)35}$ 7$\overline{)53}$ 8$\overline{)65}$ 6$\overline{)59}$

9$\overline{)74}$ 8$\overline{)67}$ 4$\overline{)22}$ 5$\overline{)46}$

Dividing Three-Digit Numbers without Remainders

How to divide a three-digit number by a one-digit number without remainders

Step 1

$$6\overline{)318}$$

Look at the first digit of the dividend (3). It is smaller than 6 so it can't be divided by 6 to produce a whole number. Next take the first two digits of the dividend (31) and determine how many 6's it contains. In this case 31 holds five 6's (5 x 6 = 30). Place the 5 above the division bracket.

$$6\overline{)318}^{\,5}$$

Step 2

Multiply the 5 by 6 and write the result (30) below the 31 of the dividend.

$$\begin{array}{r}5\\6\overline{)318}\\30\end{array}$$

Step 3

Draw a line under the 30 and subtract it from 31 (31 - 30 = 1). Bring down the 8 from the 318 and write it to the right of the 1.

$$\begin{array}{r}5\\6\overline{)318}\\\underline{30}\\18\end{array}$$

Step 4

Divide 18 by 6 and place that answer above the division bracket to the right of the five.

$$\begin{array}{r}53\\6\overline{)318}\\\underline{30}\\18\end{array}$$

Step 5

Multiply the 3 of the quotient by the divisor (6) to get 18 and place this below the 18. Subtract 18 from 18. Since the result is 0, the division is finished.

$$\begin{array}{r}53\\6\overline{)318}\\\underline{30}\\18\\\underline{18}\\0\end{array}$$

Dividing Three-Digit Numbers

Divide. Fill in the empty squares.

```
     □□□                    □□□                    □□
6 ) 6 7 8              4 ) 8 9 2              8 ) 5 3 6
     □                      □                      □□
    □□                     □□                     □□
     □                      □                     □□
    □□                     □□□                     □
     □□                     □
      □                     □
                            □□□
                            □
                            □
```

```
    □□                     □□□                    □□□
4 ) 1 9 6              3 ) 3 9 9              3 ) 4 4 1
   □□                     □                      □
   □□                    □□                     □□
   □□                     □                     □□
    □                                            □□□
                         □□□                      □
                         □
                         □
```

```
    □□                     □□                     □□
7 ) 6 5 1              3 ) 2 2 2              8 ) 5 9 2
   □□                     □□                     □□
   □□                     □□                     □□
   □□                     □□                     □□
    □                      □                      □
```

Dividing Three-Digit Numbers

Divide. Fill in the empty squares.

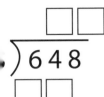
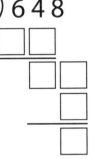
$$) \; 6\,4\,8$$

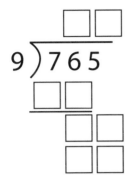
$$9 \,) \; 7\,6\,5$$

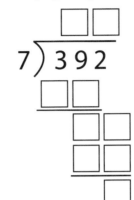
$$7 \,) \; 3\,9\,2$$

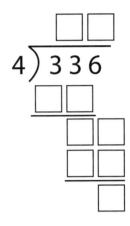
$$4 \,) \; 3\,3\,6$$

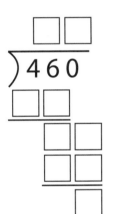
$$) \; 4\,6\,0$$

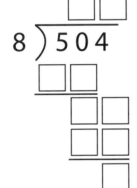
$$8 \,) \; 5\,0\,4$$

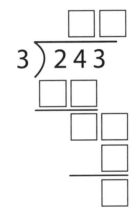
$$3 \,) \; 2\,4\,3$$

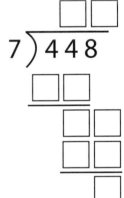
$$7 \,) \; 4\,4\,8$$

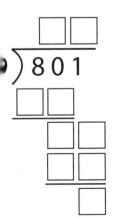
$$) \; 8\,0\,1$$

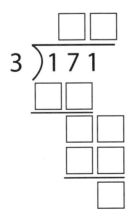
$$3 \,) \; 1\,7\,1$$

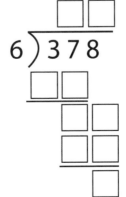
$$6 \,) \; 3\,7\,8$$

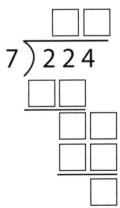
$$7 \,) \; 2\,2\,4$$

Dividing Three-Digit Numbers

Divide. Fill in the empty squares.

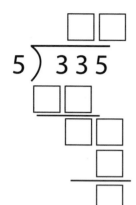

5$)$335

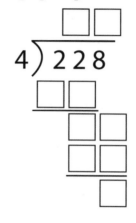

8$)$432

4$)$228

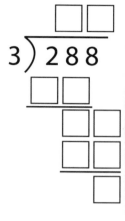

3$)$288

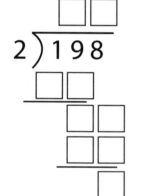

2$)$198

7$)$525

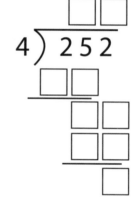

4$)$252

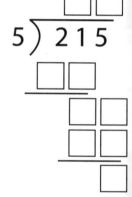

5$)$215

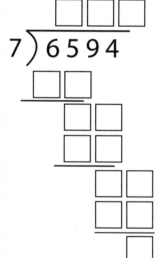

7$)$6594

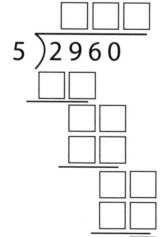

5$)$2960

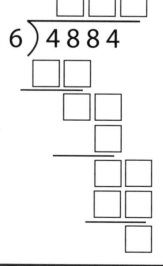

6$)$4884

9$)$2223

Long Division Without Remainders

Across

2. $288 \div 6 =$ ___
4. $160 \div 5 =$ ___
6. $255 \div 5 =$ ___
8. $328 \div 8 =$ ___
10. $96 \div 8 =$ ___
12. $132 \div 3 =$ ___
14. $216 \div 6 =$ ___
16. $164 \div 4 =$ ___
18. $186 \div 3 =$ ___
20. $74 \div 1 =$ ___
22. $116 \div 2 =$ ___
24. $126 \div 3 =$ ___
26. $90 \div 6 =$ ___
28. $96 \div 3 =$ ___
30. $440 \div 8 =$ ___
32. $266 \div 7 =$ ___
34. $106 \div 2 =$ ___
36. $130 \div 5 =$ ___
39. $216 \div 8 =$ ___
41. $144 \div 9 =$ ___
43. $224 \div 7 =$ ___
44. $176 \div 8 =$ ___
46. $200 \div 4 =$ ___
47. $165 \div 3 =$ ___
49. $108 \div 6 =$ ___
50. $96 \div 8 =$ ___

Down

1. $512 \div 8 =$ ___
3. $405 \div 5 =$ ___
5. $96 \div 4 =$ ___
7. $117 \div 9 =$ ___
9. $130 \div 10 =$ ___
11. $216 \div 9 =$ ___
13. $368 \div 8 =$ ___
15. $536 \div 8 =$ ___
17. $75 \div 5 =$ ___
19. $168 \div 7 =$ ___
21. $215 \div 5 =$ ___
23. $425 \div 5 =$ ___
25. $168 \div 8 =$ ___
27. $212 \div 4 =$ ___
29. $100 \div 4 =$ ___
31. $156 \div 3 =$ ___
33. $410 \div 5 =$ ___
35. $279 \div 9 =$ ___
37. $504 \div 8 =$ ___
38. $24 \div 2 =$ ___
40. $225 \div 3 =$ ___
42. $130 \div 2 =$ ___
45. $105 \div 5 =$ ___
48. $306 \div 6 =$ ___

Dividing Three-Digit Numbers with Remainder

You already know that when you divide smaller numbers you sometimes have a **remainder** or some left over. Many times you'll have a **remainder** when dividing larger numbers, too.

step 1

$$6\overline{)319}$$

Look at the first digit of the dividend (3). It is smaller than 6 so it can't be divided by 6 to produce a whole number. Next take the first two digits of the dividend (31) and determine how many 6's it contains. In this case 31 holds five 6's (5 x 6 = 30). Place the 5 above the division bracket.

step 2

$$6\overline{)319}^{\,5}$$

Multiply the 5 by 6 and write the result (30) below the 31 of the dividend.

step 3

$$6\overline{)318}^{\,5}$$
$$30$$

Draw a line under the 30 and subtract it from 31 (31 - 30 = 1). Bring down the 9 from the 319 and write it to the right of the 1.

step 4

$$6\overline{)319}^{\,5}$$
$$30$$
$$\overline{19}$$

Divide 19 by 6 and place that answer above the division bracket to the right of the five.

step 5

$$6\overline{)319}^{\,53R1}$$
$$30$$
$$\overline{19}$$
$$18$$
$$\overline{1}$$

Multiply the 3 of the quotient by the divisor (6) to get 18 and place this below the 19. Subtract 18 from 19. Write the **remainder**: R1

Three-Digit Numbers With Remainders

Divide. Fill in the empty squares.

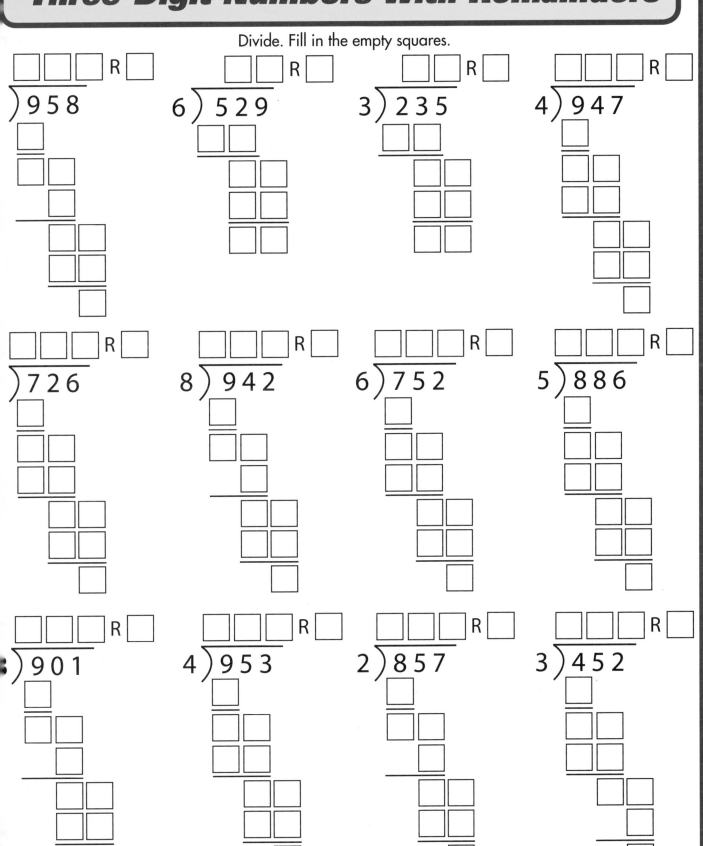

Three-Digit Numbers With Remainders

Divide. Fill in the empty squares.

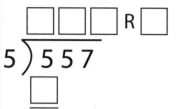

$5 \overline{)557}$

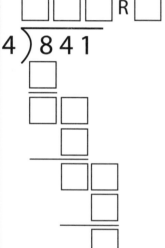

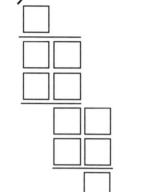

$4 \overline{)793}$

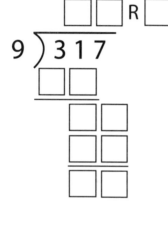

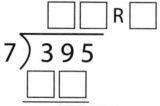

$7 \overline{)395}$

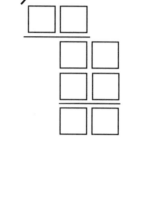

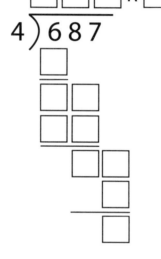

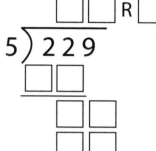

$5 \overline{)229}$

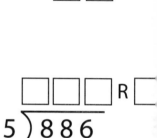

$4 \overline{)841}$

$9 \overline{)317}$

$4 \overline{)687}$

$5 \overline{)886}$

$4 \overline{)623}$

$3 \overline{)817}$

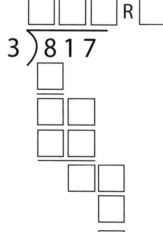

$2 \overline{)857}$

$3 \overline{)452}$

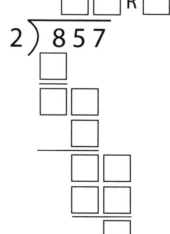

Three-Digit Numbers With Remainders

Divide. Fill in the empty squares.

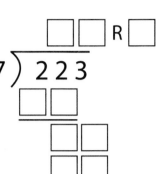

7)223

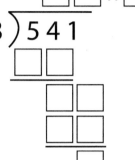

8)541

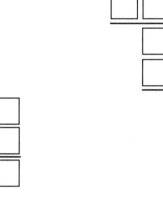

7)993

9)439

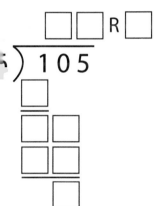

6)105

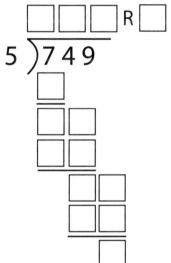

5)749

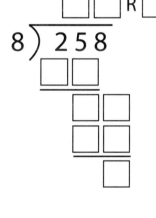

8)258

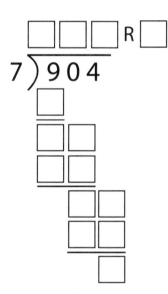

7)904

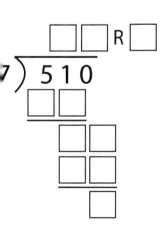

7)510

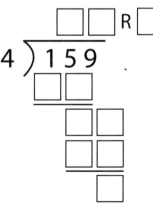

4)159

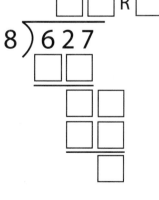

8)627

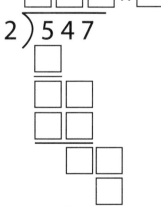

2)547

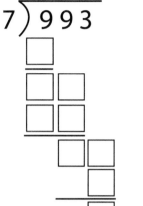

Dividing Four-Digit Numbers

Divide. Fill in the empty squares.

□□□ R □
5)1687

□□□ R □
5)1358

□□□ R □
9)2483

□□□ R □
7)3527

□□□ R □
7)4038

□□□ R □
4)2589

□□□ R □
3)1897

□□□ R □
8)6329

□□□ R □
8)4205

Greatest Quotient Game!

Practice your division skills with a group of friends. Remove the face cards and "ten" cards from a standard deck of playing cards. The Aces equal 1 and the Jokers equal 0. Each player draws a game board like this on a sheet of paper.

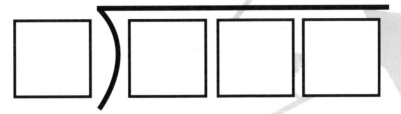

The caller selects a card and reads the number aloud. Each player writes that number in any of the boxes on his game board. Repeat until four cards have been drawn and each player's board has a one-digit divisor and a three-digit dividend.

Each player solves his division sentence. The player with the greatest quotient is the winner of the round. Play to 500 points—or any other sum you agree upon.

player 1

```
      5 9 8 r 3
6 ) 3 5 9 1
```

player 2

```
      3 0 5 5
3 ) 9 1 6 5
```

player 3

```
      5 3 9 6
1 ) 5 3 9 6
```

WINNER!

Division Pyramids

Complete the pyramids by filling in the missing **divisors** and **dividends**. Each **quotient** below becomes the next **dividend** or **divisor** above. The first one has been done for you.

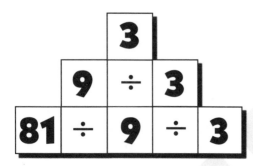

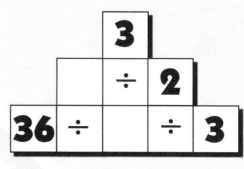

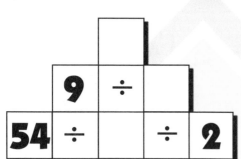

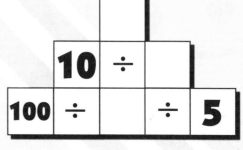

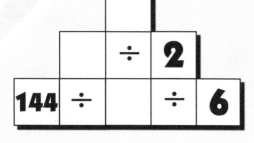

Real-Life Problem Solving

1. Stacey wants to buy several bracelets. Each bracelet costs $4. Stacey has $16. How many bracelets can Stacey buy?

2. Kyle collects the baseball bats after each game. There are 24 bats and 4 bags. How many baseball bats should Kyle place in each bag?

3. Jamie had a sleepover with 8 friends. For breakfast, Jamie's mother provided 18 doughnuts. How many doughnuts can Jamie and her friends each have?

4. The parking lot at the grocery store has a capacity for 54 cars. A maximum of 9 cars can be parked in each row. How many rows are there?

5. Mom had purchased 18 prizes for the class party. Each game would have 3 winners. How many games will be played at the party?

6. The coach provided treats for the 9 players on the team. He had 18 hot dogs and 9 drink boxes. How many hot dogs could each player have?

7. Stephanie is making caramel apples for the carnival. Her recipe made twelve caramel apples, but she made 36 caramel apples. How many times did she make this recipe?

8. Zachary and Jason bought a video game and divided the cost equally. The video game cost $24. How much did each boy have to pay for the video game?

9. There are 63 boxes of crayons to be divided equally among 7 3rd grade classrooms. How many boxes of crayons will each classroom receive?

10. The cheerleaders had a car wash to raise money for new uniforms. They charged $5 per car. If they made $45, how many cars did they wash?

Real-Life Problem Solving

1. The display at the video store has five shelves. Jacob has 60 video games to put on the shelves. How many video games can Jacob place equally on each shelf?

2. At Lauren's school, a total of 144 bags of groceries was collected last month. Each classroom collected 12 grocery bags of food. How many classrooms collected groceries?

3. Stephen dealt 52 cards to each of the four players. How many cards did each player receive?

4. Austin worked to cut a 48" board into 4 equal lengths. How long was each board?

5. A total of 54 swimmers participated in the state swim meet. Six swimmers race at one time in the preliminary heats. How many preliminary heats are necessary?

6. Kimberly has 32 pieces of equipment to distribute equally among 8 teammates. How many pieces of equipment will each teammate receive?

7. The camp activity director divided the 64 campers into 8 equal teams. How many campers were on each team?

8. The store owner received 150 CDs this morning. The CDs will be divided equally among five stores. How many CDs will each store receive?

9. Michael has 72 pieces of candy to distribute evenly into eight bags. How many pieces of candy will be in each bag?

10. There are 49 5th grade students to present their book reports. If 7 students present their reports each day, how many days will it take for all the students to present their book reports?

Real-Life Problem Solving

1. Team members sold t-shirts to their families and friends. The t-shirts cost $6 each. The team members collected $480. How many t-shirts did they sell altogether?

2. Nick scored 84, 90, 91, and 95 on the last four assignments. What is Nick's average score? (Hint: divide the total points by the number of assignments.)

3. Amanda made a chart illustrating her science fair project. She used a sheet of poster board that was 30 inches wide. She divided the poster board into six equal columns. How wide was each column?

4. A total of 255 cars was entered into the race. The entries were divided equally into three divisions. How many cars were entered in each division?

5. The gardeners worked all week to plant 360 trees equally among four locations throughout the city. How many trees were planted in each location?

6. The company purchased 96 computers to be divided equally among the six new offices. How many computers did each office receive?

7. Samantha's family drove 1,200 miles in four days. How many miles did they average each day?

8. Construction workers divided 495 pieces of lumber equally into three locations around the construction site. How many pieces of lumber were in each location?

9. There are 182 6th grade students in the school. Half of the 6th grade students went on a field trip last Thursday. Half of the students went on the field trip last Friday. How many students went on the field trip last Friday?

10. The 342 senior adults who live at Liberty Care Center are divided equally among 6 buildings. How many adults live in each building?

Real-Life Problem Solving

 1. The scouts collected 805 toys last Christmas. They distributed the toys to 7 schools. How many toys did each school receive?

 2. There will be 545 guests at the banquet. Each guest will be served one piece of cake. Each cake serves 8 people. How many cakes are needed? Will there be any cake left if each guest is served one piece?

 3. A total of 320 athletes registered for the summer games. The athletes were divided into five divisions. How many athletes were in each division?

 4. At the concert last night $5,310 was collected at the gate. Tickets were $6 each. How many tickets were sold at the gate?

 5. A total of 952 tickets were sold at the movie theater yesterday. There are 8 movies showing. What is the average number of tickets sold per movie?

 6. One quart of ice cream serves 8 persons. How many quarts will be needed to serve 48 guests?

 7. The band teacher requested that 45 chairs be set up in 5 equal rows. How many chairs will there be in each row?

 8. Michael and his family plan to drive 1,800 miles in 4 days. How many miles must they average each day?

 9. The 5th grade class is assigned to read a novel in 10 days. The novel has 160 pages. How many pages should students read each day?

 10. During practice, the coaches divided the players into 6 teams. There are 72 players. How many are on each team?

ame: _____ **Time:** _____ **Correct:** _____ **/50**

Time Test

Write the missing **dividend**, **divisor**, or **quotient**.

15 ÷ ___ = 5	24 ÷ ___ = 8	30 ÷ 5 = ___	4 ÷ 1 = ___
45 ÷ ___ = 5	18 ÷ 3 = ___	64 ÷ 8 = ___	12 ÷ 6 = ___
21 ÷ ___ = 3	15 ÷ 3 = ___	6 ÷ 2 = ___	28 ÷ 4 = ___
24 ÷ ___ = 3	81 ÷ 9 = ___	27 ÷ 9 = ___	28 ÷ 7 = ___
36 ÷ 9 = ___	40 ÷ 8 = ___	14 ÷ 7 = ___	12 ÷ ___ = 3
40 ÷ 1 = ___	36 ÷ 6 = ___	64 ÷ 8 = ___	36 ÷ ___ = 4
18 ÷ ___ = 6	25 ÷ 5 = ___	36 ÷ ___ = 6	27 ÷ ___ = 3
81 ÷ ___ = 9	24 ÷ ___ = 8	48 ÷ ___ = 8	36 ÷ 9 = ___
45 ÷ 5 = ___	28 ÷ ___ = 4	72 ÷ ___ = 9	63 ÷ 7 = ___
81 ÷ ___ = 9	12 ÷ ___ = 4	18 ÷ 3 = ___	18 ÷ 2 = ___
36 ÷ 6 = ___	16 ÷ 2 = ___	49 ÷ 7 = ___	35 ÷ 5 = ___
21 ÷ ___ = 7	9 ÷ 3 = ___	8 ÷ 8 = ___	25 ÷ 5 = ___
	27 ÷ 3 = ___	54 ÷ 9 = ___	

Time Test

Write the **quotient**.

$5\overline{)25}$ $9\overline{)36}$ $9\overline{)27}$ $8\overline{)72}$

$6\overline{)36}$ $5\overline{)20}$ $5\overline{)35}$ $9\overline{)45}$

$4\overline{)16}$ $9\overline{)63}$ $8\overline{)64}$ $1\overline{)8}$

$7\overline{)21}$ $7\overline{)7}$ $2\overline{)18}$ $8\overline{)16}$

$21 \div 7 =$ ___	$81 \div 9 =$ ___	$14 \div 7 =$ ___	$64 \div 8 =$ ___
$24 \div 8 =$ ___	$40 \div 8 =$ ___	$32 \div 8 =$ ___	$63 \div 9 =$ ___
$36 \div 9 =$ ___	$36 \div 6 =$ ___	$36 \div 6 =$ ___	$45 \div 5 =$ ___
$40 \div 1 =$ ___	$15 \div 5 =$ ___	$72 \div 9 =$ ___	$81 \div 9 =$ ___
$12 \div 6 =$ ___	$48 \div 8 =$ ___	$35 \div 7 =$ ___	$25 \div 5 =$ ___
$81 \div 9 =$ ___	$16 \div 4 =$ ___	$4 \div 1 =$ ___	$63 \div 7 =$ ___
$25 \div 5 =$ ___	$64 \div 8 =$ ___	$12 \div 6 =$ ___	$15 \div 5 =$ ___
$15 \div 3 =$ ___	$6 \div 2 =$ ___	$28 \div 4 =$ ___	$24 \div 8 =$ ___
	$27 \div 9 =$ ___	$21 \div 3 =$ ___	

78

ame: **Time:**   **Correct:**   **/50**

Time Test

Write the **quotient**.

$9\overline{)81}$	$5\overline{)45}$	$6\overline{)36}$	$3\overline{)15}$	$6\overline{)24}$
$5\overline{)5}$	$4\overline{)16}$	$2\overline{)18}$	$6\overline{)36}$	$8\overline{)32}$
$9\overline{)18}$	$8\overline{)32}$	$4\overline{)36}$	$7\overline{)28}$	$5\overline{)35}$
$9\overline{)36}$	$1\overline{)8}$	$2\overline{)18}$	$9\overline{)54}$	$7\overline{)21}$
$2\overline{)14}$	$9\overline{)27}$	$6\overline{)36}$	$8\overline{)16}$	$9\overline{)9}$
$7\overline{)42}$	$8\overline{)64}$	$1\overline{)7}$	$7\overline{)49}$	$3\overline{)9}$
$4\overline{)16}$	$8\overline{)32}$	$9\overline{)63}$	$5\overline{)25}$	$5\overline{)40}$
$4\overline{)12}$	$1\overline{)6}$	$2\overline{)16}$	$9\overline{)27}$	$8\overline{)40}$
$8\overline{)32}$	$7\overline{)35}$	$3\overline{)21}$	$8\overline{)64}$	$4\overline{)24}$
$9\overline{)54}$	$4\overline{)20}$	$8\overline{)36}$	$8\overline{)72}$	$4\overline{)28}$

79

Name: | **Time:** | **Correct:** | **/5**

Time Test

Write the **quotient**.

10)120   12)132   11)110   12)96   11)33

11)55   12)60   10)80   11)99   12)84

12)72   12)144   11)121   10)20   12)132

11)77   12)108   12)12   10)100   12)48

110 ÷ 10 = ___   10 ÷ 10 = ___   33 ÷ 11 = ___   70 ÷ 10 = ___   90 ÷ 10 = __

144 ÷ 12 = ___   60 ÷ 12 = ___   55 ÷ 11 = ___   84 ÷ 12 = ___   96 ÷ 12 = __

66 ÷ 11 = ___   72 ÷ 12 = ___   40 ÷ 10 = ___   36 ÷ 12 = ___   30 ÷ 10 = __

110 ÷ 11 = ___   48 ÷ 12 = ___   50 ÷ 10 = ___   96 ÷ 12 = ___   77 ÷ 11 = __

120 ÷ 12 = ___   88 ÷ 11 = ___   144 ÷ 12 = ___   60 ÷ 10 = ___   108 ÷ 12 = __

99 ÷ 11 = ___   132 ÷ 12 = ___   121 ÷ 11 = ___   24 ÷ 12 = ___   30 ÷ 10 = __

me: **Time:**   **Correct:**   **/50**

Time Test

Write the **quotient**.

$\overline{)21}$	$12\overline{)72}$	$9\overline{)36}$	$12\overline{)60}$	$3\overline{)18}$
$\overline{)54}$	$11\overline{)33}$	$7\overline{)28}$	$4\overline{)16}$	$12\overline{)84}$
$\overline{)36}$	$5\overline{)40}$	$11\overline{)132}$	$10\overline{)90}$	$12\overline{)132}$
$\overline{)30}$	$7\overline{)49}$	$12\overline{)108}$	$10\overline{)110}$	$6\overline{)42}$

$\div 3 =$ ___	$40 \div 8 =$ ___	$33 \div 11 =$ ___	$144 \div 12 =$ ___	$8 \div 8 =$ ___
$\div 12 =$ ___	$27 \div 3 =$ ___	$96 \div 12 =$ ___	$16 \div 2 =$ ___	$55 \div 11 =$ ___
$\div 6 =$ ___	$121 \div 11 =$ ___	$36 \div 12 =$ ___	$48 \div 6 =$ ___	$72 \div 9 =$ ___
$\div 11 =$ ___	$20 \div 5 =$ ___	$88 \div 11 =$ ___	$35 \div 7 =$ ___	$24 \div 8 =$ ___
$\div 12 =$ ___	$15 \div 5 =$ ___	$36 \div 9 =$ ___	$54 \div 6 =$ ___	$30 \div 6 =$ ___
$\div 11 =$ ___	$8 \div 4 =$ ___	$120 \div 10 =$ ___	$7 \div 7 =$ ___	$27 \div 9 =$ ___

Name: **Time:**   **Correct:**

Time Test

Write the **quotient**.

11)‾44‾	12)‾84‾	3)‾24‾	5)‾60‾	3)‾36‾
12)‾144‾	7)‾35‾	4)‾28‾	10)‾80‾	9)‾45‾
5)‾25‾	12)‾36‾	10)‾120‾	9)‾27‾	9)‾81‾
7)‾35‾	10)‾70‾	12)‾108‾	12)‾132‾	6)‾48‾

18 ÷ 3 = ___	64 ÷ 8 = ___	36 ÷ 12 = ___	24 ÷ 12 = ___	8 ÷ 1 = ___
15 ÷ 5 = ___	72 ÷ 9 = ___	66 ÷ 11 = ___	12 ÷ 2 = ___	18 ÷ 9 = ___
9 ÷ 3 = ___	120 ÷ 10 = ___	8 ÷ 4 = ___	54 ÷ 6 = ___	72 ÷ 8 = ___
100 ÷ 10 = ___	20 ÷ 4 = ___	32 ÷ 8 = ___	49 ÷ 7 = ___	8 ÷ 8 = ___
84 ÷ 12 = ___	15 ÷ 3 = ___	36 ÷ 4 = ___	12 ÷ 12 = ___ 36	32 ÷ 4 = ___
88 ÷ 11 = ___	16 ÷ 4 = ___	50 ÷ 10 = ___	÷ 6 = ___	25 ÷ 5 = ___

Practice Test

Write the **quotient**.

$6\overline{)35}$ $\quad$ $9\overline{)33}$ $\quad$ $2\overline{)25}$ $\quad$ $4\overline{)60}$ $\quad$ $6\overline{)68}$

$6\overline{)46}$ $\quad$ $3\overline{)97}$ $\quad$ $5\overline{)90}$ $\quad$ $2\overline{)50}$ $\quad$ $5\overline{)61}$

$5\overline{)37}$ $\quad$ $8\overline{)27}$ $\quad$ $5\overline{)14}$ $\quad$ $2\overline{)92}$ $\quad$ $4\overline{)63}$

$9\overline{)82}$ $\quad$ $8\overline{)57}$ $\quad$ $4\overline{)22}$ $\quad$ $4\overline{)33}$ $\quad$ $7\overline{)54}$

Practice Test

Write the **quotient**.

$2\overline{)122}$ $5\overline{)235}$ $7\overline{)546}$ $9\overline{)558}$ $8\overline{)432}$

$4\overline{)284}$ $3\overline{)87}$ $5\overline{)425}$ $2\overline{)126}$ $5\overline{)360}$

$8\overline{)680}$ $4\overline{)252}$ $3\overline{)267}$ $3\overline{)135}$ $6\overline{)432}$

$6\overline{)33}$ $6\overline{)87}$ $2\overline{)38}$ $6\overline{)55}$ $6\overline{)73}$

Practice Test

Write the **quotient**.

$2\overline{)568}$ $\qquad$ $5\overline{)891}$ $\qquad$ $6\overline{)745}$ $\qquad$ $8\overline{)628}$ $\qquad$ $7\overline{)349}$

$3\overline{)157}$ $\qquad$ $3\overline{)222}$ $\qquad$ $8\overline{)308}$ $\qquad$ $8\overline{)704}$ $\qquad$ $3\overline{)362}$

$5\overline{)195}$ $\qquad$ $2\overline{)360}$ $\qquad$ $3\overline{)504}$ $\qquad$ $6\overline{)199}$ $\qquad$ $8\overline{)721}$

$5\overline{)405}$ $\qquad$ $5\overline{)620}$ $\qquad$ $2\overline{)488}$ $\qquad$ $8\overline{)821}$ $\qquad$ $5\overline{)144}$

Practice Test

Write the **quotient**.

$5\overline{)505}$ $8\overline{)872}$ $3\overline{)629}$ $6\overline{)754}$ $9\overline{)981}$

$7\overline{)149}$ $6\overline{)433}$ $8\overline{)708}$ $5\overline{)158}$ $5\overline{)295}$

$5\overline{)325}$ $4\overline{)612}$ $4\overline{)284}$ $8\overline{)378}$ $6\overline{)432}$

$3\overline{)600}$ $9\overline{)541}$ $5\overline{)415}$ $3\overline{)213}$ $6\overline{)73}$

Practice Test

Write the **quotient**.

$3\overline{)177}$ $9\overline{)378}$ $7\overline{)756}$ $8\overline{)576}$ $2\overline{)126}$

$8\overline{)112}$ $8\overline{)656}$ $4\overline{)360}$ $7\overline{)147}$ $5\overline{)180}$

$9\overline{)108}$ $8\overline{)144}$ $3\overline{)216}$ $8\overline{)240}$ $8\overline{)336}$

$4\overline{)272}$ $8\overline{)382}$ $6\overline{)450}$ $7\overline{)224}$ $9\overline{)540}$

DIVISION-OES!

DIVISION-OES plays like dominoes. Carefully cut out the cards on pages 89-95. Each card has a division sentence on one end and an answer to a different division sentence on the other end. Players match a correct answer to a division sentence, forming domino-style patterns. To play, each player draws five cards. Place one card face up in the center of the table. Place the remaining cards face down on the table, in a box or in a bag. On your turn, match a correct answer from a card in your hand to a division sentence on the table. If you cannot make a match, select another card from the draw pile and end your turn. The player who plays all his or her cards first is the winner. Or, if no more cards can be played, the winner is the player with the least number of cards left in his or her hand.

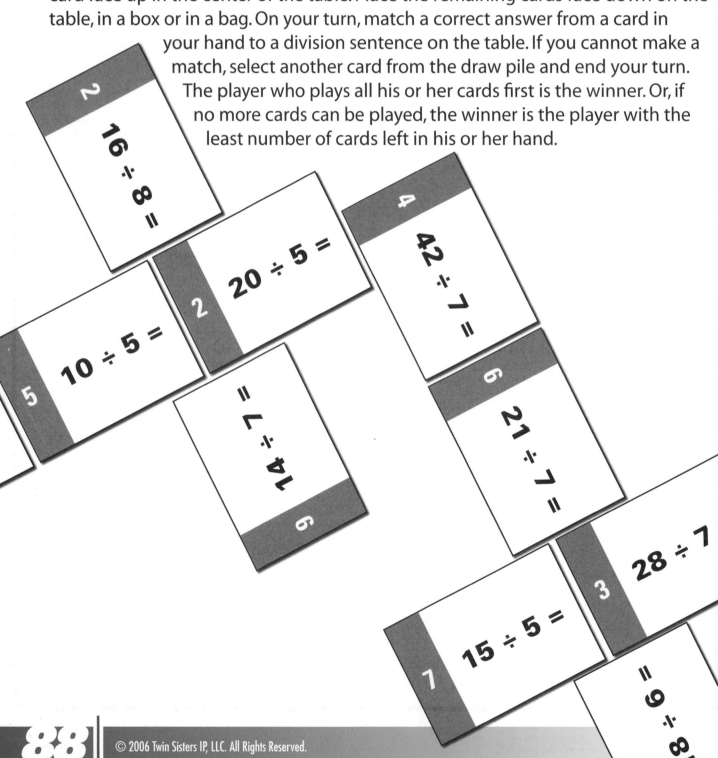

$2 \div 2 =$	6	$4 \div 2 =$	2	$6 \div 2 =$	7	$8 \div 2 =$
$10 \div 2 =$	4	$12 \div 2 =$	6	$14 \div 2 =$	5	$16 \div 2 =$
$18 \div 2 =$	8	$3 \div 3 =$	3	$6 \div 3 =$	1	$9 \div 3 =$
$12 \div 3 =$	1	$15 \div 3 =$	4	$18 \div 3 =$	7	$21 \div 3 =$
$24 \div 3 =$	6	$27 \div 3 =$	5	$4 \div 4 =$	3	$8 \div 4 =$
$12 \div 4 =$	12	$16 \div 4 =$	1	$20 \div 4 =$	8	$24 \div 4 =$
$28 \div 2 =$	3	$32 \div 4 =$	9	$36 \div 4 =$	4	$5 \div 5 =$

This page was intentionally left blank for the DIVISION-OES activity to be completed.

10 ÷ 5 =	**7**	15 ÷ 5 =	**2**	20 ÷ 5 =	**4**	25 ÷ 5 =
30 ÷ 5 =	**9**	35 ÷ 5 =	**3**	40 ÷ 5 =	**5**	45 ÷ 5 =
6 ÷ 6 =	**2**	12 ÷ 6 =	**8**	18 ÷ 6 =	**5**	24 ÷ 6 =
30 ÷ 6 =	**5**	36 ÷ 6 =	**11**	42 ÷ 6 =	**3**	48 ÷ 6 =
54 ÷ 6 =	**1**	7 ÷ 7 =	**9**	14 ÷ 7 =	**6**	21 ÷ 7 =
28 ÷ 7 =	**12**	35 ÷ 7 =	**4**	42 ÷ 7 =	**10**	49 ÷ 7 =
56 ÷ 7 =	**6**	63 ÷ 7 =	**9**	8 ÷ 8 =	**2**	16 ÷ 8 =

This page was intentionally left blank for the DIVISION-OES activity to be completed.

$24 \div 8 =$	7	$32 \div 8 =$	3	$40 \div 8 =$	2	$48 \div 8 =$
$56 \div 8 =$	1	$64 \div 8 =$	5	$72 \div 8 =$	8	$9 \div 9 =$
$18 \div 9 =$	9	$27 \div 9 =$	2	$36 \div 9 =$	7	$45 \div 9 =$
$54 \div 9 =$	8	$63 \div 9 =$	6	$72 \div 9 =$	4	$81 \div 9 =$
$10 \div 10 =$	3	$20 \div 10 =$	1	$30 \div 10 =$	9	$40 \div 10 =$
$50 \div 10 =$	10	$60 \div 10 =$	5	$70 \div 10 =$	3	$80 \div 10 =$
$90 \div 10 =$	4	$100 \div 10 =$	9	$110 \div 10 =$	7	$120 \div 10 =$

This page was intentionally left blank for the DIVISION-OES activity to be completed.

11 ÷ 11 =	5	22 ÷ 11 =	6	33 ÷ 11 =	3	44 ÷ 11 =
55 ÷ 11 =	1	66 ÷ 11 =	11	77 ÷ 11 =	10	88 ÷ 11 =
99 ÷ 11 =	6	110 ÷ 11 =	12	121 ÷ 11 =	2	132 ÷ 11 =
12 ÷ 12 =	3	24 ÷ 12 =	7	36 ÷ 12 =	9	48 ÷ 12 =
60 ÷ 12 =	8	72 ÷ 12 =	1	84 ÷ 12 =	5	96 ÷ 12 =
108 ÷ 12 =	6	120 ÷ 12 =	9	132 ÷ 12 =	4	144 ÷ 12 =

This page was intentionally left blank for the DIVISION-OES activity to be completed.